Health, doctors and
social workers

Library of Social Work

General Editor:
Noel Timms
Professor of Social Work Studies
University of Newcastle upon Tyne

Health, doctors and social workers

Zofia Butrym and John Horder

Routledge & Kegan Paul
London, Boston, Melbourne and Henley

First published in 1983
by Routledge & Kegan Paul plc
39 Store Street, London WC1E 7DD,
9 Park Street, Boston, Mass. 02108, USA,
296 Beaconsfield Parade, Middle Park,
Melbourne, 3206, Australia, and
Broadway House, Newtown Road,
Henley-on-Thames, Oxon RG9 1EN
Printed in Great Britain by
Redwood Burn Ltd, Trowbridge, Wilts.

Library of Congress Cataloging in Publication Data

Butrym, Zofia.

Health, doctors, and social workers.
(Library of social work)
Includes bibliographical references and index.
1. Social medicine.   I. Horder, John, 1919–
II. Title.   III. Series.
RA418.B87 1983   362.1'042   82–23169

ISBN 0–7100–9403–5

Contents

Acknowledgments

We owe a great debt of gratitude to the many individuals who have shown an interest in our undertaking and who have helped us by contributing ideas and case material, and by offering criticism. These include the following: Thelma Stollar, honorary lecturer in medical social work at the London Hospital Medical School, June Neill of the National Institute for Social Work, Ruth Heller of the Polytechnic of the South Bank, Joan Patton, Ruth Rhees, Pauline Rowe, Elizabeth Ashton, Elizabeth Daly, William Horder, Pamela George, Eric Oram – social work practitioners – and Professor Michael Shephard, Drs Ian Gilchrist, Len Ratoff, Alexis Brook, Caryle Steen, and S.J. Chouksey – general practitioners.

Our special thanks are due to Mary Sherlock who has helped to edit the final version, Marjorie Cummins who undertook a large part of the secretarial work and Anne Deakins who typed the manuscript.

We should also like to record our indebtedness to the many patients/clients who have trustingly shared their problems with us, and thus provided invaluable opportunities to gain more insight into the nature and range of human difficulties and the most effective means of resolving or relieving them.

Chapter 1

The purpose and plan of the book

PURPOSE

This book is primarily addressed to social workers,
although its subject equally concerns doctors and others
engaged in health care. The authors, a social worker and
a general practitioner, have in mind especially those in
training or who have recently qualified, and who have had
little experience of social work in relation to health problems. We wish to introduce social workers to common and
important medical problems, to discuss psychological and
social implications and to suggest appropriate social work
interventions. A second purpose is to discuss the ways in
which doctors think, comparing their approach with that of
social workers. By this means we hope to uncover some of
the causes of misunderstandings which still exist between
two vitally important helping professions, whose objectives
and tasks are closely related.

The book is thus not primarily intended for the specialist
'medical' social worker whose knowledge of the issues discussed must be assumed. Its overall purpose is to provide
relevant insights into health problems and what constitutes
an appropriate response to these for the use of 'generalist'
social workers, particularly those in situations where
health problems are a factor.

But why should such social workers know something about
medicine and doctors? They have more than enough to learn
in a short time about a multiplicity of other matters, many of
a more obvious and immediate relevance to social work.
Why ask them to concern themselves with another profession's subject and expertise? Why not subscribe to a strict
division of labour, concentrating the knowledge and skills

1

of the social worker on social work and of doctors and
nurses on medicine? Is it not dangerous for social workers
to know a little about medicine and for doctors to know a
little about social work? Would it not be better to leave the
understanding of medical problems entirely to doctors and
nurses, and of the presonal/social problems to social
workers?

   We believe that the answer is 'no', because the medical
and psycho-social problems of individuals and families are
so often inextricably inter-related that attention to any one
aspect of the problem without due reference to the others is
bound to be of limited value. So each profession needs to
be capable of recognising those elements which constitute
the area of special concern and expertise of the other.
Separate expertise is not synonymous with a total ignorance
of the other's field; on the contrary, such ignorance leads
to narrow-mindedness and a restriction of the opportunities
of providing the most appropriate forms of help to patients/
clients. Would social workers really wish doctors and
nurses to know nothing about the personal and the social
problems facing their patients or what social workers can
do to alleviate these? And surely the opposite holds true?
We therefore believe that effective collaboration between
doctors and social workers, without which the needs of many
of their respective patients and clients would not be met,
calls for a degree of mutual understanding of tasks and
expertise.

   In addition we would argue social workers must not opt
out of an informed interest in health matters. The title of
the present work refers deliberately to 'health' in preference to 'medicine'.

   It must already be apparent that we subscribe to a holistic conception of health, acknowledging the significance of
the economic, the environmental, the social, the psychological, and the cultural factors in health in addition to the
biological ones traditionally associated with it. Health
care in our view is not the exclusive domain of doctors and
nurses but concerns all citizens who bear a degree of responsibility by their behaviour and mode of life for their own
health and that of their community. Therefore, as increasingly in our complex and troubled world health-care issues
assume new and perplexing dimensions calling for some very
difficult decisions, it follows that a greater participation by
the public is called for. The creation within the National
Health Service structure of Community Health Councils is

one tangible sign of a growing recognition of the need for more sharing of information and responsibility.

Social workers' active involvement in health issues is important for two reasons: first, the potential value of the social work contribution to the problems of sick and disabled people and their families; and second, social workers can play an informed, responsible part in both social debate and in social action to improve health-care provision.

We hope that this book may offer some help in both these respects, although its primary focus is on direct work with those who have health problems.

Even this focus has necessitated a strict selection of subject matter for discussion. This is not intended to be a comprehensive textbook of medicine for social workers. It is an introduction concentrating on those medical problems which illustrate best the role of the social worker in medical situations and the opportunities for co-operation between social workers and doctors. In addition selected medical problems which are common and important at the present time are discussed. Too much is omitted for this to be a book of reference. To fill the gap, guidance on further reading is offered at the end of each chapter.

PLAN

Our philosophy in relation to health, coupled with our objective to provide social workers with some relevant information and understanding about health problems without overwhelming them with technical detail, has led to a multipronged approach instead of the more conventional form of presentation based on classification by medical diagnosis. Therefore, whilst we have retained this latter form of classification in Chapter 6, we have in addition introduced several other ways of marshalling the material.

The two case studies in Chapter 3 illustrate both the bio-psycho-social nature of health problems and the ways in which the extent and the quality of the collaboration between doctors and social workers influence the effectiveness of the help offered. In Chapters 4 and 5 we look at ill health from the perspectives of age and of symptom respectively.

Chapters 7 and 8 are concerned with the implications for medicine and social work of differing kinds of health problems in various health-care settings.

In Chapter 2 we describe the differences in the nature of

the contributions made to health care by doctors and social
workers and we attempt to highlight both the potential
strengths of these differences and the ways in which they
lend themselves to mutual misunderstandings or destructive
conflict.

SUGGESTIONS FOR FURTHER READING

The broad approach to health we have adopted calls for a
thorough understanding of the various factors influencing
human functioning and of their interaction.
    Reynolds, V. (1976), 'The Biology of Human Action',
W.H. Freeman, is a most useful discussion of the biological,
psychological and social influences on human action and a
survey of relevant research. The unifying theme in these
different perspectives is the relationship between the human
capacity for adaptation to changing circumstances and the
constraints imposed by man's limitations in dealing with
stress resulting from such change.
    Our inevitably incomplete list of medical conditions can be
supplemented by reference to:
    'An International Classification of the Health Problems of
Primary Care' (1976), Occasional Paper I, Journal of the
Royal College of General Practitioners.
    Many of the gaps in social worker's knowledge of medical
terminology and of the meaning of particular conditions can
be filled by the use of a good medical dictionary. We
recommend:
    'Black's Medical Dictionary', latest revised edition.
    A recently published guidebook specifically designed for
use by social workers is also likely to prove helpful:
    Halliburton, P. and Quelch, K. (1981), 'Get Help – A
Guide for Social Workers to the Management of Illness in
the Community', Tavistock Publications.
    A radical critique of the medical approach to health is:
    Illich, I. (1976), 'Limits to Medicine', Boyar. This
book, however, contains some important philosophical
reflections on the characteristics of health and disease in
the context of a holistic view of human nature.
    A recent more balanced discussion of the place of medi-
cine in health care and of the problematic nature of some of
its current functions, is to be found in the Reith Lectures
for 1980 published as:
    Kennedy, I. (1981), 'The Unmasking of Medicine', Allen
& Unwin.

The following recent governmental or government-sponsored reports emphasise the effects of economic and social factors on health and its care:

'Report of the Royal Commission on the National Health Service' (the Merrison Report) (1979), Cmnd 7615, HMSO.

DHSS (1976), 'Prevention and Health: Everybody's Business', HMSO.

DHSS (1976), 'Fit for the Future: Report of the Committee on Child Health Services' (the Court Report), Cmnd 6684, HMSO.

DHSS (1980), 'Inequalities in Health', HMSO.

The nature of the contribution of social work to health care is discussed specifically in:

Report of the DHSS Working Party (1974), 'Social Work Support for the Health Service' (the Otton Report), HMSO.

Chapter 2

Collaboration between doctors and social workers

THE AIMS OF MEDICINE

Sir George Newman (1) states:
  There are four questions which in some form or other
  every patient asks his doctor:
  (a) What is the matter with me?   This is Diagnosis.
  (b) Can you put me right?   This is Treatment and
  Prognosis.
  (c) How did I get it?   This is Causation.
  (d) How can I avoid it in future?   This is Prevention.
    He may not be called upon to attempt a full answer to
  his patient, but he must give a fair working answer to
  himself.
  To answer such questions in the innumerable contexts in
which they are presented to doctors, medicine has amassed
a very considerable body of technical knowledge increasing
and refined over centuries.   In the last three hundred
years, and especially in the last one hundred, it has profi-
ted greatly by the scientific method, with its rigorous
testing of theories.   Many branches of knowledge using
this method contribute to the doctor's capacity to answer
these questions.   Anatomy, physiology, biochemistry and
pathology are among those most frequently applied, but
chemistry, physics and mathematics are fundamental contributors too.   One of the aims of medicine is to apply knowledge and skills derived from all the sciences and increasingly also from the humanities.   They are brought to bear
on the consultation, the process of which is described in
the next section.
  Newman refers to the tasks of combating disease and
helping sick people, but many doctors see medicine as

concerned with unhappiness as well as with disease and
with social malfunctioning, especially if this results from
sickness or causes sickness. Indeed restoration to normal
social functioning, i.e. return to normal duties at work or
in the home, is usually the criterion marking the end of a
disease. There are nevertheless many people who continue
working in less than their normal state of health because
for psychological, economic or social reasons they cannot
afford to 'go sick'. (2) It must also be acknowledged that
there are some doctors whose exclusive allegiance to the
organic/scientific model of medicine (in contrast to the
holistic model we expounded), makes them neglect the psychological and social causes and effects of ill health because
they view these as aspects of human functioning lying outside
the province of medicine.

The promotion and maintenance of health is another aim of
medicine. Doctors' ability to achieve this depends on
understanding the causes which threaten health, i.e. the
causes of defective development, disease, injury, unhappiness and social failure. Relatively little is known, however, about the causes of most human afflictions. What
knowledge is available can be used either through public
health measures, like the protection of food and water, the
inspection of the industrial environment, vaccination and
immunisation programmes, or through the education of individuals about personal hazards to health such as smoking or
overeating and, more positively, the value of physical
exercise and how to deal with excessive stress.

The aims of medicine can thus be summarised as the care
of sick and injured people, the diagnosis and cure of disease, its prevention, and the promotion of health.

THE AIMS OF SOCIAL WORK

It can be argued that the aims of social work are even wider
than those of medicine, and that its relative strengths and
weaknesses, as compared with those of medicine, are partly
derived from this fact.

Social work is concerned with the promotion of social
functioning by individuals, families, and local community
groups. This emphasis on social functioning carries
important implications. Firstly, it implies that social work
is concerned neither with people in isolation from their
material and social environment, nor with the environment

by itself; its focus lies in the interaction between the two.
Secondly, the very width of the concept of social functioning
implies that a very important task facing all social work
practitioners is to convert their broad aims into more
tangible practical objectives. This by no means easy task
is open to varying interpretations derived from differing
values and priorities. In addition, social workers do not
have complete autonomy in deciding what they should be
doing. A large part of their social mandate is derived from
specific legislation and they are mostly employed in large
bureaucratic organisations. Moreover because of the relative youth and insecurity of their profession, social workers
are particularly open to the influence of others – politicians,
administrators, doctors, magistrates, etc.

It is becoming increasingly important that social workers
define their role more clearly, particularly in respect of
the various legislative powers with which they have been en-
trusted by society. Such definition, to be appropriate,
must integrate professional ideals with organisational realities. This demands that social workers become more explicit than previously about their own values and skills and the
implications of these for what they can and cannot do. However, such a clear stance is not easy to adopt in a society
which prides itself on the pluralism of its value systems.

Despite these current ambiguities and uncertainties, we
believe that the following aims of social work would be
generally accepted by both the social work profession and
the public:

(a) To help people who experience a variety of problems in
their social functioning, who are unhappy in various ways
and to varying degrees or who antagonise others by their
behaviour and their failure to fulfil their social roles.
This involves an informed assessment of their problems
followed by action designed to resolve or ameliorate them
where possible, or where not, to make living with them more
bearable;

(b) To prevent unnecessary human suffering by means of
early and appropriate intervention to stop problems escalat-
ing;

(c) To promote social well-being through informed social
action.

There is thus nothing inherently incompatible between the
aims of social work and those of medicine: on the contrary,
their fundamental affinity is striking.

THE WAYS IN WHICH DOCTORS THINK

The central and most typical activity in medicine is the consultation. Although some doctors are rarely involved in consultations, such as pathologists concerned in laboratory work or community physicians concerned with health and disease as it affects large groups and populations, the consultation with the sick individual remains the chief focus of the work of most doctors. It is an appropriate starting point to discuss ways in which doctors think.

The object of the consultation for the patient is to receive help in trouble. The object for the doctor at least as an ideal inculcated in training is to 'make a diagnosis'. The doctor's aim is therefore narrower than the patient's, but more precise and purposeful. The distinction immediately accounts for some misunderstandings between doctor and patient to be discussed later. The purpose of making a diagnosis is, to help the patient.

The patient complains: 'I have a cough'; 'I can't sleep'; 'I have a terrible pain, what is it, doctor?'; 'Johnny keeps getting colds'. For the trained doctor each of these raises a range of possibilities and the object is to narrow down this range to one disease if possible. Essentially diagnosis aims to achieve the naming of one disease, which will explain the facts which the patient offers or the doctor elicits by questions and tests. The same diagnosis will provide, through training and experience, the essential guidelines for managing and, if possible, curing the disease.

The range of possibilities suggested by the complaint 'I have a cough' stretches from the common cold or smoking, at one end, to cancer of the lung and tuberculosis at the other. Questions will often be enough to decide the correct diagnosis with a high degree of probability, but sometimes physical examination and special tests, such as chest X-ray, will be needed. Although doctors often have to depend on probability alone, they seek for certainty, as does the patient. If the patient has been coughing for only three days and started a sore throat and running nose two days before that, it is highly probable that he has a cold. If the episode is closed within a total of ten days, this probability becomes a virtual certainty and no special tests are needed. If a cough has persisted for six weeks and there is no past history of cough and the patient is a heavy smoker, nothing short of a physical examination and chest X-ray will exclude the possibility that the patient has a cancer in a bronchial

tube or lung. Even more elaborate and unpleasant tests,
like a bronchoscopy (insertion of a tube into the bronchial
tree through which the interior of the bronchus can be illum-
inated and examined by direct vision) may be needed to reach
certainty in a matter which can mean life or death, now that
surgical treatment for this condition has some limited
success.

Diagnosis of a disease means a one- or two-word label:
'Bronchitis', 'Pneumonia', 'Bronchial Carcinoma'. Each of
these words, in addition to implying a pattern of symptoms
(cough, pain in the chest) and physical signs (moist sounds,
heard with a stethoscope) and abnormal test results (an abnormal shadow on a chest X-ray or a positive bacteriological culture) also implies a recognisable pathology. If a
patient dies of pneumonia (now a rare event), a post-mortem
examination will reveal an abnormal state of one or both
lungs - essentially that they are solid and airless. Examination of the abnormal tissues under the microscope will
reveal other more detailed evidence of the pathology.

In addition to implying a 'clinical picture' and a pathology,
a diagnosis suggests management. Training and experience
tell a doctor that pneumonia responds and is usually cured
by an antibiotic. Testing the sputum against a range of
antibiotics in the laboratory may reveal that the bacteria
which afflict Mr Smith are killed by tetracycline, but not
by penicillin. The essential weapon in the battle to cure
Mr Smith's pneumonia is now clear and the doctor can prog-
nose or forecast that without treatment Mr Smith would be
ill for about two months, with a fifty-fifty chance of dying;
with tetracycline, he will recover within a week.

The progress of the case then acts as a check to prove or
disprove the process of thought which led to diagnosis.
Occasionally, a fact missed or the presence of another unsuspected disease will mean that prognosis of recovery
within a week will not be borne out. Pneumonia occasionally occurs round an unsuspected cancer of the lung. In
this case recovery may be slow or incomplete and a further
diagnostic process must be undertaken.

This description of the diagnostic process has been in
ideal terms but concise diseases are diagnosed correctly,
the correct prognoses are made and treatments lead to cure
as everyday events. Unfortunately, not all disease is
curable. If the doctor, through the symptoms and signs in
the nervous system, finds evidence of multiple sclerosis,
his patient and he face a long-term problem which medicine

can scarcely touch and which will slowly deteriorate.
Care not cure is the appropriate word.   Medicine still has
to supply care more frequently than cure, but most medical
students and young doctors accept this hard fact with difficulty.

A second problem about the diagnosis of diseases is that
not all people consulting doctors have any disease.
Patients consult sometimes because they are anxious,
depressed, lonely or in conflict with another person, or
have some lifelong difficulty of personality.   To apply the
diagnostic process in these instances is more problematic.
True, one can through the same eliminating process reach a
diagnosis 'no organic disease'; and this is some help, at
least to the doctor.   One can reach a label 'depression' or
'personality problem'.   The difference in these last two
instances is that there is no known and agreed pathology and
no clear indication for management.   To extend the diagnostic process developed in relation to physical disorders to
the psychological and social disorders stretches its usefulness.   It still has value in these contexts but something
more or different is required: attempting an imaginative
entry into the other person's experience, rather as a bio-
grapher, in order to understand its meaning and significance for him.

A third difficulty is that the diagnostic process treats the
doctor as a neutral investigator, whereas the consultation
involves a relationship between two human beings.   The
doctor's personality, as well as his interview technique,
necessarily exert considerable influence upon what happens.
The impact of the doctor's personality is both unavoidable
and potentially valuable.   Different doctors have different
purposes in life, different personal difficulties, different
styles and different ways of appealing or repelling; these
play a part which cannot be discounted.   They can also
positively help.   It is not just good interviewing technique
which helps a person to talk about his very personal problem to a stranger, but also the latter's personality and
approach to him as a fellow human being.

To find the patient's problem, then solve it: this should
be the essence of the doctor's aim in the consultation.
There are of course many problems that can be defined, but
not solved.   Unfortunately the most difficult sort of consultation for most doctors is the one which can only end in the
realisation that the patient wants something, but that there
is absolutely nothing the doctor can do.   It takes time for

young doctors to learn that it may matter as much or even
more to the patient that the doctor should be there, continue
to be there and be someone who is dependable, than that he
should do something.

Social workers used to helping the client 'help himself'
notice that it is the doctor who seeks to solve the problem
himself on his patient's behalf. Typically medical problems
– those which demand technical intervention like an antibiotic
to cure an infection – will indeed require this, but when
problems are psychological or social in origin, a different
approach is usually required; this, the social worker's
approach, does not come easily to doctors, whose training
points to decision and action by the doctor himself or by his
co-workers.

THE ORIGINS OF MEDICAL THINKING

The practice of medicine is a very old tradition, constantly
subjected to new influences. The rapidity of change in
knowledge and skills which challenges all doctors today
should not obscure traditional elements which remain important. Historically medical thinking and practice has three
major origins: religion, pragmatism and the sciences. In
ancient civilisations, as in some contemporary cultures the
same person combines the function of doctor and priest without obvious difficulty. Many elements in modern medical
practice and in social work have religious roots. Fear of
sickness and death is the business of priests as well as
doctors in our own society; it tends to discover religious
feelings in the least religious people. The concern of
doctors (as of social workers) for the individual's welfare,
sometimes to the point of personal sacrifice, seems to relate
to the idea of the intrinsic worth of the human person which
is to be found in the Judaeo-Christian ethical tradition.
Hospitals are still run by nuns acting as nurses in a number
of other European countries. The Hippocratic oath, which
remains influential, stems from the religious tradition of
ancient Greece.

By pragmatism one means the assemblage of knowledge
and skills through practical experience. Many remedies
still used in medicine were discovered because a tried solution appeared to have an effect in relieving a symptom.
Opium and digitalis, still very important remedies, were
discovered in this way, and the discovery of penicillin

involved a comparable element of chance. The mould of
penicillin settled on one of the plates on which Fleming was
culturing bacteria; where it settled the bacteria dis-
appeared; but Fleming's mind was prepared to make use of
the observation through years of experiment in search for
just this sort of agent. Anti-depressive drugs were discovered because one of them was in use as an effective
remedy against the tubercle bacillus. It was the observation that tuberculous patients receiving this drug were surprisingly cheerful that led a psychiatrist to try them on very
depressed patients. The disadvantage of the pragmatic
approach in medicine is that it is very patchy, relying on
unrelated chance observations, and that it gives rise to
many false hopes. It is indeed the basis of quackery.
Remedies have always owed a part of their effect to the fact
that the sick person wants a medicine to work. That one
patient claims recovery after taking a particular remedy
does not prove that this is effective for others or that it has
any inherent healing quality.

The third, and increasingly important element in medical
thinking is science, particularly the physical and biological
sciences, distinguished from other bodies of knowledge by a
method of thinking. For a statement of any sort to count as
science, it must be possible to prove it or disprove it,
whether by observation or experiment. 'Dogs have two
eyes' is a statement which can be verified by looking at dogs.
'Unselfishness ennobles man' is a statement which can be
neither proved nor disproved. The first statement is scientific, the second is of a moral nature. In demanding evidence and proof, science brings a scepticism which must be
contrasted with faith. The latter is vital to religious and
moral thinking, but is an inappropriate, indeed dangerous,
feature of the scientific approach.

One of the more important contributions of scientific
thinking to medicine is the double-blind controlled trial of a
remedy. This device is necessary to verify whether a new
remedy is better than an old, and one that is inert better
than no remedy at all. Neither doctor nor patient must
know whether the substance administered contains the
remedy or not. So the doctor cannot be influenced by his
own bias in hoping that the remedy will work, because he
will not know what the patient received. The need for
these elaborate precautions is clearer if it is realised that
a proportion of people develop reactions to neutral substan-
ces including such symptoms as headache, vomiting, or even
a rash.

Apart from a method of thinking, the sciences have provided much of the knowledge and skills which medicine borrows for its practice in the consultation, the hospital ward, or operating theatre. Medicine is an amalgam of knowledge and skills based on many different sciences and other contributions: physical, chemical, biological, psychological and sociological. The science of pathology, with its branches such as bacteriology and haematology, has emerged more specifically in answer to medical needs. But in the final analysis medicine itself is an applied rather than a basic science.

MEDICAL EDUCATION

The link between medical practice and its sources of knowledge, skills and attitudes is medical education. This brings old traditions and new discoveries to the doctor in a process which starts at school and ends with retirement.

The undergraduate period of five years or six years ends in a university degree. The object is to create a 'basic' doctor requiring further training in the chosen branch of the profession. This further training always combines education and practice, as it is aimed at producing specialists capable of carrying increasing responsibility for their work. Those doctors who intend to be general practitioners now share the obligation to take special postgraduate training.

The division of the undergraduate period into pre-clinical basic sciences and clinical subjects is now becoming blurred in most medical schools. Anatomy, physiology, biochemistry, psychology and sociology need to be related to human beings if they are to be meaningful to medical students. Similarly the practice of neurology or genito-urinary surgery or psychiatry should be closely related to its scientific roots when first presented to students. The purpose was well stated by the Royal Commission on Medical Education. (3)

The aim of medical education should be to produce, at graduation, a person with two essential qualifications. He should have, first, a knowledge of the medical and behavioural sciences sufficient for him to understand the scientific basis of his profession and to permit him to go forward with medicine as it develops further; and secondly, a general introduction to clinical method and patient care in the main branches of medicine and surgery, together with an introduction to social and preventive medicine. We hope that the student will be taught throughout in such a way as to inculcate in him a desire to continue learning not only during the postgraduate training but throughout his professional life.

Medical education has tended in the past to be rather narrow. Its start in the three scientific subjects biology, physics and chemistry at school can be criticised. It has tended to be an intensive process of learning facts; the increasing volume of facts and skills collected by each of thirty special branches which all claim the right to contribute has created a major problem. But the increasingly rapid rate of replacement of old knowledge and skills by new, derived from the ever-developing scientific bases of medicine, has forced a new look on medical education. The young doctor has to be trained for a lifetime of changing knowledge and changing tasks. He now has to learn how to assimilate and assess new ideas, rather than to learn facts and skills for a lifetime usage - how to think rather than what to know.

WAYS IN WHICH SOCIAL WORKERS THINK

The origins of social work are difficult to trace because its roots lie in the self-help activities of families and communities. Social work came into formal existence only when these activities proved inadequate in dealing with the problems created by industrialisation and urbanisation. The beginnings of modern social work are usually associated with the Charity Organisation Society established in the second half of the nineteenth century to make the relief of poverty outside the Poor Law rational and 'scientific'.

The raison d'être of social work has always been its concern for the well-being of the individual, and in the pursuit of this objective the influence of morality derived from both Judaism and Christianity has been considerable. The strong value orientation of early social work, coupled with the absence of any 'hard' knowledge about human needs and functioning, led at times to a highly moralistic approach, evidenced, for example, in early editions of 'The Charity Organisation Review'. However, leading social workers were invariably concerned to give their work a sound foundation of knowledge. It is perhaps for this reason that social workers have tended at various times to embrace somewhat indiscriminately the latest theoretical formulation, for example, psycho-analysis during the inter- and early post-war years, and sociology more recently.

The relationship in social work between the elements of 'heart' and 'head' has been the subject of controversy throughout its history. Some emphasised the former, others tended to minimise the importance of personality and motivation. However, the great majority of social workers always saw the two as complementary and focused on finding appropriate ways of fostering both.

The interdependence of the 'feeling' and the 'thinking' components in social work stems from its primary concern – human well-being expressed in social functioning. Social workers see their primary role as helping people with various problems encountered in living. They are guided in their attempts by certain basic assumptions about human nature and needs. These can be summed up briefly as the worth of individuals, their right to respect, and their need for contact with others as an essential means of achieving self-fulfilment.

On these assumptions much attention is given by social workers to the meaning of a client's experiences to himself. Clients are both sources of information and primary contributors to resolving their own problems. The interview, therefore, plays an essential part as a medium both for understanding clients and their problems and for offering help. The interview is the social work equivalent of the medical consultation, but it incorporates most of its diagnostic activities within its own context. There is no equivalent in social work to laboratory tests by which the nature of a problem can be identified.

Social workers, like doctors, need to understand a problem before they can intervene in it appropriately. How can this be achieved in the absence of any clear connections of cause and effect? The difficulties inherent in social assessment are considerable, but not insurmountable. They demand of the worker a respect for knowledge, a strong motivation for its acquisition, and sufficient trust in his or her own judgment and integrity to allow action in the absence of complete certainty (which in social work is unobtainable). Social assessment has to be viewed as an ongoing process, subject to constant modifications. For this reason, in contrast to medicine, assessment and treatment are not clearly separable processes; they proceed simultaneously in varying degrees throughout, complementing each other.

Social work relies for its theoretical base on knowledge borrowed from a variety of disciplines, particularly the behavioural and the social sciences. The absence of a separate body of knowledge is a cause of concern to some. They fail to appreciate the intellectual autonomy, creativeness and challenge inherent in the selection and application of knowledge. Moreover, some social workers are afflicted by a sense of inferiority endemic in the social sciences and derived from excessive reliance for the verification of knowledge on the model of the natural sciences. They should be guided instead by the concept of scientific activity which Professor Waddington, among others, has put forward. (4) He emphasised the importance of the material under study dictating the means adopted for its study, and not vice versa. The material with which social workers are working is human nature interacting with its physical and social environment. This clearly calls for a varied range of approaches, some concerned with objective and verifiable facts, others having to do with the subjective reality of people's perceptions and feelings. It is this latter requirement which gives the worker/client relationship a central place. It is only through such a relationship, and the attributes which it incorporates, that the reality of personal meanings can be gauged and responded to. It is also only within the context of such a relationship that acceptance, respect, empathy, psychological support and hope - all of which the large majority of social workers' clients require - can be conveyed.

Although social work makes use of material forms of help such as domiciliary services, day or residential care, additional financial resources, much of their value to clients rests in the quality of the relationship within which these services are provided.

It is not only people with a low sense of personal adequacy who require help in dealing with their feelings. The need for meaningful communication and the resulting confirmation of personal identity is inherent in human nature. Many in our society suffer from a surfeit of utilitarian and 'dispensable' relationships, but lack authentic ones, in which they are valued and accepted unconditionally. Any form of deficiency in social functioning, for whatever reason, creates dependency on others and makes people extremely vulnerable psychologically to those on whose help they rely; this calls for great consideration and delicacy of treatment.

The importance of the quality of the helping relationship has always been recognised in social work, and social workers have quite properly claimed a degree of expertise and skill in this area.   If social work were ever to lose this expertise or devalue its importance, it would change beyond recognition and would lose its raison d'être.

Another factor which makes social-work practice so dependent on the quality of the worker/client relationship is its commitment to helping people to find their own solutions. This precept is based not only on the value of respect for persons, which precludes attempts at organising other people's lives for them; it is also derived from the very practical realisation that, given the nature of the problems in which social workers intervene, the ultimate judges and experts in resolution must usually be the clients themselves. The role of the social worker is largely that of clarifier, comforter, educator, guide, information provider, adviser, supporter and 'broker'.   As we have already suggested, this reliance in social work on self-help by the client is a point of contrast with the role of the doctor as frequently carried out at present.

The fact that social workers do not completely take over the solution of problems from clients (something not always sufficiently recognised by the public or even by colleagues from other helping disciplines) does not mean that they have no views as to what constitutes appropriate and right behaviour in different circumstances.   Social workers are not, cannot be, amoral.   Social work concerned with the nature and quality of human living cannot fail to be involved with issues of good and evil.   It is important for social workers and for everybody else to be clear about this: respect for other people's opinions and for their autonomy in reaching decisions depends on the professional being clear about his own stance and maintaining security in the face of opposing values and opinions.

EDUCATION FOR SOCIAL WORK

The requirements of relationship skills and wide-ranging knowledge about human nature, social structures and legislation makes education for social work very demanding. Some demands are even contradictory, as for example, the

need to promote sensitivity for the feelings of others,
together with self-awareness, and the need for a sharpening
of observational powers, together with an objective weighing
up of 'external' evidence.

One of the problems besetting social work education
(although this can also be seen as a strength) is the absence
of a generally agreed pattern. One may qualify as a social
worker on a two-year non-graduate course, a four-year
undergraduate course, or by taking postgraduate training
for one or two years depending on the nature of the first
degree. This multiplicity of entry routes, and a virtual
absence of any differentiation in responsibilities after training and of a limited availability of professional supervision
or consultation, creates a situation in which many people,
including doctors, find it difficult to know what they can
expect of a social worker. The differences in knowledge,
skills and effectiveness on the part of different social
workers encourages a perpetuation of the view of social
work as something some people are born with and others not,
rather than a professional activity which can be mastered
through education and practice. The problem is increased
by the expansion in demand for social work in recent years
and the creation of many more posts than there were trained
people to fill them; thus large numbers of holders of designated social work posts have in fact no formal training in
social work. Such a situation is highly unsatisfactory for
the clients; in social workers it encourages an attitude of
scepticism about the value of professional education and it
can lead to demoralisation. There are, however, currently
encouraging signs that awareness of the problem and the
will to do something about it are growing, and that remedies
in the form of a clearer delineation of tasks, and possibly
some form of accreditation, will soon be put into operation.

A current dilemma concerns specialisation. The former
specialities such as medical and psychiatric social work,
child care and probation, were based to a large extent on
the criterion of agency function rather than of special problems or distinct knowledge and skills. As a result they
came into disrepute following the Seebohm reorganisation,
as both fragmenting and duplicating the help available to
families. Whatever the validity of these criticisms, there
have been considerable losses to offset the gains. The
enthusiasm for 'genericism' during the early post-Seebohm
era obscured the need for social workers to have some
specific focus in their work if they are are to avoid being

'Jacks of all trades'. This has resulted in the loss of
former expertise in some directions, notably in work with
mentally disordered people, and with the sick and the disabled; in some areas the quality of social work offered to
clients in these groups has suffered as a result.

Currently specialisation is again becoming 'respectable'
and some employing authorities have begun to encourage it
by designating specialist posts. The educational provisions
for specialisation are, however, inadequate. Basic
courses qualifying for social work should emphasise the
common elements of knowledge and skill, as these are a
necessary foundation from which specialisation must develop.
On the other hand, in the absence in social work of the
equivalent to house posts or specialist traineeships in medicine, it is not very clear how specialisation following on
generic education will develop, although a range of post-
qualifying courses is gradually becoming available. This
is one of the most urgent issues at present, on the resolution of which the future of the profession greatly depends.

ISSUES OF COLLABORATION BETWEEN MEDICINE AND
SOCIAL WORK

Our two accounts of how doctors and social workers think,
how they practice and what education they receive, reflect
the different origins, roles and status of the two professions.

The origins of both medicine and social work lie in humani-
tarian ethics derived from religion, and from empirical observation sifted by experience. This gives them an important shared base.

The major difference between medicine and social work
rests on the use of 'science', i.e. the extent of the adoption
of a rigorous intellectual approach based on the demand that
ideas be capable of proof and verification. In the course of
the last three centuries medicine has attained both scientific
respectability and a degree of certainty in being able to
identify many of the cause/effect connections so vital to
both diagnosis and treatment.

In contrast, social work has largely relied on the contribution of the various social sciences. These have provided
it with a much more tenuous and shifting base where facts
and opinions are often intertwined. The greater reliance
in social work on the subjective factors in human life has
meant that opinions held and conclusions reached regarding

the nature of individual problems and the most appropriate
way of responding to them were often impossible to verify
and hard to defend in the face of scepticism or challenge.
In this respect social worker's reluctance to make use of
empiricism by drawing on their rich practice experience has
been a serious drawback (as has been their relative failure
to make use of research).

It is this difference in the status of the knowledge base in
the two disciplines which has been a major factor in the
problem of communication and collaboration between doctors
and social workers, as Garrad has well argued. (5)   The
more scientific the medicine, the more derogatory of social
work it has tended to be, and the less secure the social
work the more awe-inspired and ambivalent towards medicine
it has been.

Nevertheless, medical knowledge is by no means complete:
it resembles a net consisting of holes as well as threads, of
vast patches of ignorance and of relatively small threads of
knowledge.   Doctors are far from being able to understand,
cure or prevent all the diseases of mankind: recent successes such as open heart surgery or the varoius organ trans-
plants, could mislead both doctors and patients about the
limitations of medicine.   Under the influence of the physical
and pathological sciences an effective but narrow approach
has come to dominate much of the medical consultation, aimed
above all at achieving a 'diagnosis' which can be stated in
one or two words, classified, related to morbid changes
which can be demonstrated in life or after death by objective
tests and which point the ways of management aimed at cure.
In the right context this approach serves its purposes
admirably.   It has come to be known as the 'medical model'
and we have described it in detail because of its dominating
influence.   It is a formidable tool alongside which the
'social assessment model' of social work reveals a striking
lack of precision.

The weakness of the medical model lies in its limited
range of application.   As discussed in Chapter 1, while it
is possible to say that doctors should be concerned exclusively with physical disorders, leaving everything else to
other professionals, this would leave them unable to understand, explain or cope with a considerable proportion of
apparently physical disorders.   It would also prevent them
from either understanding or satisfying those patients with
problems which extend far wider than the merely physical
problems originating in feelings, thoughts, relationships,

economic and social pressures. Our discussion of pain in
Chapter 5 provides an illustration of this point. Doctors
can only confine themselves to the physical if they make
themselves blind to the rest.

Doctors are increasingly aware that neglect of the psychological, economic or social aspects of medicine makes for
inferior practice. But when they do struggle with psychological and social problems they are faced with the same difficulties as social workers, with the additional handicap that
their well-tried tool of scientifically based objectivity no
longer serves so well, or not at all.

Like social workers, they find themselves in situations
where uncertainty prevails, yet decisions have to be made,
where the relation between cause and effect is obscure;
where diagnosis, if it is possible at all, becomes a gradual
process subject to constant modification as the case develops
and as the patient produces information which may have been
forgotten or too painful to reveal earlier; where assessment
and treatment proceed simultaneously; where one- or two-
word labels are meaningless and nothing less than a bio-
graphical statement serves; where problems can be stated
but no solution found; where action is not only impossible
but irrelevant and where the real need is for emotional support; where the posture of mental objectivity is shattered
and the doctor like anyone else finds that he is still a human
person with vulnerable feelings of his own which are not
easy to control; where humility is demanded if it is not
already a habitual characteristic. So doctors, like social
workers, sometimes find themselves out of their depth,
needing to use a variety of approaches, only some of which
rely on objective verifiable facts, whilst others have to
depend on the subjective reality of people's perceptions and
feelings, including their own.

Such an extension of the concerns of medicine has brought
it much closer to social work. One could argue in fact that
the past problem of indifference, derived from separate concerns and perspectives may be replaced by the problem of
rivalry resulting from much shared ground. Whether or not
such a danger materialises will depend on the degree of
realisation by both groups that their respective contributions are complementary and that the effectiveness of their
help to patients/clients will increasingly depend on their
success in establishing satisfactory collaboration. Such a
recognition of mutual dependence will call for considerable
adaptations; both groups will have to become more ready to

give and receive in a relationship of mutual respect, trust and sharing.   There is considerable potential for both medicine and social work to reinforce each other once they recognise the strengths derived from their different bases of operation and approach.   Thus social workers can enhance their practice by learning from doctors a more disciplined approach to the process of assessment and helping.   Doctors can benefit in their understanding of patients and their problems by drawing on some of the skills social workers have developed in using a relationship as the major medium for understanding the more subjective aspects of a problem and for offering help of a less tangible kind where there is no 'simple' solution.

There is no easy formula, however, for achieving successful collaboration between doctors and social workers. It can only come about gradually from the experience of working together and thus learning at first hand each other's strengths and limitations, and what benefits can accrue to patients/clients from such teamwork.   Such direct experience could be the best way of counteracting the negative stereotypes often held by members of each profession of the other.   The important starting point is, of course, a shared 'service orientation' which puts the needs of the patient/ client before any vested interests of a personal or professional nature.   The ethical codes of practice of both professions should help to make such a 'service orientation' a clear expectation and requirement.   Joint opportunities for study and discussion are an important means of building on that starting base.   Other relevant factors, especially those relating to organisational structures, will be discussed in Chapter 8.   The thought on which we whould like to conclude this chapter, however, is that in the context of a holistic perspective on health and its care, a case needs to be made <u>against</u> the need for a close collaboration between medicine and social work rather than for it.

SUGGESTIONS FOR FURTHER READING

The following books provide a fuller discussion of the nature of medicine and social work; and of the educational requirements for the two professions:

Z.T. Butrym (1976), 'The Nature of Social Work', Macmillan.

Central Council for the Education and Training in Social

Work (1981), 'Guidelines for Courses leading to the Certi-
ficate of Qualifidation in Social Work'.
J. McCormick (1979), 'The Doctor, Father Figure or
Plumber', Croom Helm.
Given our emphasis on the values component in both medi-
cine and social work, we list below the Codes of Practice of
both and further useful references on medical-social ethics:
British Association of Social Workers (1973), 'A Code of
Ethics for Social Work'.
British Medical Association (1980), 'Handbook of Medical
Ethics', BMA.
A.V. Campbell (1972), 'Moral Dilemmas in Medicine',
Churchill Livingstone.
R.S. Downie and E. Telfer (1980), 'Caring and Curing',
Methuen.
The following references deal more specifically with the
issues relating to collaboration between doctors and social
workers:
R. Huws-Jones (1971), 'The Doctor and the Social Ser-
vices', Athlone Press.
J. Ratoff, A. Rose and C. Smith (1974), Social Workers'
and General Practitioners' problems of working together,
'Social Work Today', 14 November.
'Education for Co-operation in Health and Social Work'
(1979), Occasional Paper 14, Journal of the Royal College
of General Practitioners.

Chapter 3

Interacting factors in health care — two illustrations

INTRODUCTION

In pursuit of the major purposes of the book - to introduce
social workers to some medical problems; to discuss their
psycho-social implications and to suggest appropriate
social work intervention, the present chapter offers two
case-illustrations with commentary on both the health problems and the social-work response.   In addition, we hope
that this chapter will demonstrate particularly clearly our
main theme in Chapters 1 and 2, namely that the concept of
medical treatment and care includes not only the physiological aspects of a person but the psychological and social
features also.

   The limitations of an exclusively organic model of health
care which treats the human body as if it were a complex
machine are being increasingly recognised.   The definition
of health in the preamble to the constitution of the World
Health Organisation - 'Health is a state of complete physical, psychological and social well-being, and not merely
the absence of disease' - illustrates a contrasting approach
which is adopted throughout this book.   Granted that an
absolute degree of well-being is unattainable by most people
at most times in their lives, this view provides an important
foundation for a practical acknowledgment of man's bio-
psycho-social nature and of the complexity of his needs and
problems.   For example, the human capacity for reflection
about the past, the present and the future results at times
in worry, anxiety and guilt, and has profound significance
for health.   Food, shelter and material goods of all kinds,
however great their importance, cannot of themselves
ensure well-being in the absence of that sense of inner

satisfaction which is derived from personal fulfilment. In this, satisfactory and trustworthy relationships with others play an essential part.

Another important characteristic of human behaviour is that it has moral aspects (not to be confused with religion or with any one particular philosophical outloon on life). Morality helps people to order their lives in ways which meet their own particular needs for fulfilment and happiness, but which are also compatible with human dignity and a sense of responsibility towards othrs.

In attending to a person's health needs, it is therefore necessary to attempt to understand personal worries and aspirations, family and other important relationships, the meaning to a person of his various social worlds, and other aspects of his life; to understand his physiology is not enough.

Thus, for example, a patient may lack the necessary motivation for rehabilitative effort following a stroke. This may be due to his loss of a sense of purpose in life as a result of strained family relationships, or, alternatively, he may have experienced for the first time in many years the care and attention of those near to him so that the secondary gains of his disablement are greater than the prospect of struggling to become more independent again.

Another patient with a stroke may suffer, by contrast, from frustration and anger because he is offered too little opportunity to overcome the residual effects of his condition. This may be due to his physical location which makes frequent attendance for physiotherapy difficult, or the lack of resources in the area such as speech therapy. It may, however, be due to a misjudgment of his determination to get better, resulting in a low priority given to his rehabilitation by his doctors and others (or, alas, to poor quality of the treatment and care given).

The difference between being ill and being sick, in the sense of the 'sick-role', is also very relevant. The term 'sick-role' refers to the formal recognition by the person himself, his doctor, the family, the employer, and others, that he is to be regarded and treated differently on account of his incapacity to function in his usual social roles. The change of status is usually indicated by a certificate of incapacity which formalises the position and entitles him to appropriate benefits. However, as Robinson has shown (1), there are many intervening factors between the person becoming ill and his 'going sick'. If two people have the same disease and both feel equally ill, it does not necessarily follow that both will 'go sick'. Different people have different ideas and make different decisions about the degree of illness which entitles them to 'go sick'. These are in turn influenced by a variety of personal family, economic and social factors. Some individuals have to weigh up the relative risks of carrying on whilst ill or 'going sick', if, for example, they fear the loss of their job, or there is no one to take over their responsibilities. Doctors, too, will vary in their judgments.

In approaching any human situation therefore the interaction of the 'inner' and the 'outer' factors, of the 'subjective' and the 'objective' elements, has to be considered before appropriate action can be determined. While a holistic health orientation on the part of doctors and the psycho-social functioning perspective of social workers can ensure its recognition, only an increasing sense of their joint responsibility will lead to a close collaboration and the resolution of the barriers between them.

THE CASE OF MR HARRISON

Cerebrovascular accidents and hypertension

Hypertension – blood pressure raised outside the normal range for a person's age – is one of the very few abnormalities of which a person may be completely unaware. It is important only because of the complications which can arise. If blood pressure remains abnormally high for a period of years, it can combine with other influences to hasten a degeneration of blood vessels which occurs in most people in old age. Several distinct illnesses result, depending mainly on the part of the body first affected by a blocked or burst artery.

Illness results from damage to the affected organ. It is the brain which is affected by a stroke and the effects may be loss of control of a limb, loss of power in muscles, loss of sensation in the skin, on one side of the face or in one arm or one leg (hemiparesis). If a particular part of the brain is damaged, speech will be affected. Consciousness may be lost temporarily. If the blood vessel affected is not only large but its blockage or severance is also sudden, death may occur at the time of the stroke.

The effects of a stroke are seen on the side of the body

opposite to the side on which the brain is damaged, because the nervous connections to the trunk and limbs cross over near the base of the skull.

The outlook for the patient with a stroke is at first completely unpredictable. Damage may be transient – an hour or so – or permanent, lifelong. The only indication on which a forecast can be made is the rate of recovery, as days and weeks go by. Complete recovery from total paralysis of a limb is possible, and improvement can continue after many months or even after a year or two. To what extent recovery is affected by the nature of the physical damage and repair or to what extent by the patient's will and effort to aid recovery are questions impossible to answer. Motivation to recover does seem to play a significant part, and cautious optimism, combining encouragement and practical help from physiotherapy, speech therapy and occupational therapy, is therefore always worthwhile. Unjustifiable promises about recovery must, however, be avoided.

Referral and medical situation

Mr Harrison, aged 61 years, the owner/manager of a factory producing leather goods, was admitted to a London teaching hospital as an emergency with a right-sided cerebrovascular accident and a resultant left-sided hemiparesis.

He was referred to the hospital social worker by the consultant because of the implications of the diagnosis, and also because he was proving to be a very 'difficult' patient in the ward. This, in addition to antagonising the hospital staff (nurses in particular), was making the management of his condition much more difficult.

Social work with Mr and Mrs Harrison

In the course of Mr Harrison's six weeks' stay in hospital the social worker was seeing him regularly once or twice weekly. She was also seeing his wife at visiting times and, following Mr Harrison's discharge, visited the couple on several occasions in their home. Her understanding of their problems and the complex dynamics of their relationship to each other and to the outside world evolved gradually as she came to know them and to be trusted by them.

Indeed trust proved to be an aspect of central significance

in this instance. Mr Harrison's previous life experiences
had provided him with ample grounds for not trusting people
readily - he was a Polish Jew who was imprisoned by the
Germans in Auschwitz concentration camp during the Second
World War. There he saw massive exterminations of fellow
prisoners and he himself expected to die on every day of the
many months spent there. On becoming free and then on
arriving in Britain, he was determined to make a fresh
start in life and to become fully independent as soon as possible. He worked hard and built up a successful business.
Latterly, however, as a result of inflation and industrial
strife, his business had been going less well and he worried
about it a good deal.

Following Mr Harrison's stroke and his admission to the
hospital, his wife was not able to continue on her own and
so they decided to wind up the business. This decision met
with difficulties and Mrs Harrison did not find it easy to extract money from the various retailers and to manage generally in her husband's absence. The situation was imposing
considerable additional strain on both Mr and Mrs Harrison
and on their relationship.

However, the ward staff were either unaware of these
facts or unable fully to appreciate their significance. When
the social worker first entered the picture, she found a
widespread attitude of hostility mixed with exasperation
towards Mr and Mrs Harrison. He was described to her by
the nurses as being 'the end' - excessively demanding of
attention and showing little consideration towards them.
Mrs Harrison was seen as encouraging Mr Harrison's dependency by being far too protective towards him and for doing
too much for him, instead of encouraging him to help himself.
For example, she would feed him, instead of making him
exercise his paralysed arm by feeding himself. She was
also accused of bringing her own food from home and thus
sabotaging the hospital's efforts to keep Mr Harrison on an
appropriate diet. The ward staff were also clearly irritated
by Mr Harrison's overt expression of feelings such as frequent weeping, loud shouts when in discomfort, and general
failure to keep a 'stiff upper lip'. Such behaviour was both
a manifestation of a different cultural background which
allowed and even encouraged a free vent to emotions, and
one of the effects of a stroke, which frequently causes
emotional lability even in previously self-controlled persons.

The lack of rapport between Mr Harrison and the ward
staff had resulted in a vicious circle: the more intolerant

and impatient the doctors' and nurses' attitudes were, the
more demanding and regressed Mr Harrison's behaviour
became, leading in turn to increased exasperation on the
part of the staff.

It was Mrs Harrison who provided the social worker with
the most dramatic illustration of this process. She told her
that on a Sunday evening, at around 10 p.m., Mr Harrison
had suddenly felt unwell and experienced difficulty in
breathing. He called a nurse and told her of this. Her
response to this complaint was to tell him that she could
assure him that he was not dead yet! Mr Harrison's reaction to this 'reassurance' was to telephone his wife in a
great panic, causing her to rush to the hospital straight-
away, where she found him in tears. A doctor was sum-
moned and he dealt with the situation to their satisfaction,
but the harm was done.

The social worker's task in this situation was complex.
As she came to know and to understand the couple, she gave
her interpretations of the case to her hospital colleagues.
The most important aspect in her opinion had to do with Mr
Harrison's need for dependence. Far from relishing
dependence, which was the superficial image he presented,
Mr Harrison, as a result of his war-time experiences and
the personality upon which they were superimposed, could
only feel secure when he was master of his own destiny.
It was the threat which dependence constituted for him
which made him react so badly to it and become excessively
demanding. His insatiable demands reflected his lack of
trust that his basic needs would be adequately met and his
past experience explained his pronounced suspiciousness.
This even extended on one or two occasions to his opposing
his wife and the social worker meeting without him being
there. The situation demonstrates the futility and the
counter-productive nature of the rebuffs which Mr Harrison
received from the ward staff, however much one appreciates
the latter's frustration.

In addition to interpreting the patient's behaviour to her
colleagues, the social worker also attempted to meet some
of Mr Harrison's needs for dependence herself, so as to
decrease his demands on the nursing staff. Her role in the
hospital lent itself particularly well to this. Not being
involved in attending to his basic physical needs, she was
a 'safer' person for him to relate to; it was easier for her
than for the doctors or the nurses to get in touch with the
'adult part' of his personality and to support that part in her

interviews with him.   She did this by encouraging him to
engage in constructive planning of his future and by assuring
him of her help and support in whatever actual steps he might
decide to take.   By emphasising that it was his future which
was being planned for and that his views and his decisions
regarding it were of paramount importance, the social
worker tangibly and expressly recognised and encouraged
Mr Harrison's independence.

She also enabled him to relive in the safe context of his
interviews with her some of his earlier experiences and
fears, and to leave them behind.   Some of these sessions
were very painful and highly charged emotionally.   Mr
Harrison recounted some of his most traumatic concentra-
tion-camp experiences and his many different losses,
including that of self-esteem.   He wept profusely and uncon-
solably at times and the social worker found it extremely
distressing to witness so much sadness and suffering.   Her
conviction, however, about the therapeutic value of such
reminiscing and reliving to Mr Harrison sustained her in
these efforts.

She was also meeting Mrs Harrison regularly, as she was
convinced that she needed as much help as the patient did.
The couple had only been married for just over two years,
Mr Harrison's first wife having died several years before.
It looked as if one of the attractions in this marriage was
the complementarity of Mr Harrison's marked independence
and Mrs Harrison's need to be dependent.   The reversal of
roles made necessary by the stroke had imposed a severe
strain on both parties.   Thus it became increasingly clear
to the social worker that, as in his relationships with the
ward staff so also with his wife, Mr Harrison's problems
about dependence played a major part.   His great reliance
on her daily visits, in spite of the very long and tiring journey and her preoccupation with the winding up of his business, his insistence on being fed and generally pampered by
her, were reflections of a basic lack of security on his
part.   Mrs Harrison's apparently limitless devotion to her
husband, her ready criticisms of his treatment by the hospital, her insistence on bringing him her own food and all the
other manifestations of her concern, were soon found to
contain ingredients of concealed resentment at having to be
the head of the family and at all the giving she had been
forced into.

The situation was potentially dangerous from the point of
view of the future relationship between the couple.   In the

view of the social worker, one way in which such danger
could be minimised was for her to offer Mrs Harrison a
considerable amount of support in coping with her new responsibilities. She did so by acknowledging the difficulty of
her position, by recognising the many sacrifices she was
making for her husband and by offering help over the practical arrangements for Mr Harrison's return home when the
time became ripe for this.

These plans by the social worker in working with the
Harrisons were put into jeopardy by his premature and
precipitate discharge home during one weekend when the
social worker was away for a few days. Although she and
the rest of the treatment team were in regular touch in discussing future plans for the patient, the hospital staff had
reacted uncritically to Mrs Harrison's request to have her
husband back home soon and failed to recognise her ambivalence over this and her anxiety about her managing to look
after him on her own. It may well be that the social worker
had contributed to the problem by failing to convey clearly
enough to her medical and nursing colleagues the nature of
her work with Mrs Harrison. Equally, it would be naive
not to assume that Mr Harrison's unpopularity on the ward
played its part. This premature discharge proved disas-
trous. Both Mr and Mrs Harrison panicked on leaving the
security of the hospital. He regressed to a state of infant-
like dependency (including double incontinence) whilst she
became harassed and resentful to the point of total prostration. After three days Mr Harrison had to be readmitted in
a sorry physical and psychological state. Rather surprisingly, however, the damage proved temporary and short-
lived. This time everyone at the hospital was determined
to manage the next discharge better and to co-ordinate their
plans and activities. The social worker was given a central role, and both the physiotherapist and the occupational
therapist who had been working with Mr Harrison consistently (and successfully) throughout his hospital stay were
actively involved in his discharge plans. This proved a
very important factor in the enhancement of Mr and Mrs
Harrison's security because they had great confidence in
the help of both physiotherapy and occupational therapy,
and so the continued availability of these treatments following return home was of great importance. Regular visits
by a community nurse were also arranged, as well as follow-
up appointments at the local hospital.

The social worker realised that this couple would need

ongoing social-work help to assist them in their adjustment
to their new mode of life and changed roles. She also knew
that she herself could not continue to work with them on
account of the distance of their home from the hospital.
The effectiveness of the transfer of Mr and Mrs Harrison
to a social worker in their local area would depend on her
success in terminating her own relationship with the couple
in a way which would feel constructive to them and which
would not make them feel abandoned or disposed of in a
routine fashion. She also realised that the couple could
only take so much at a time and that their most immediate
task was to readjust to home life. She therefore continued
seeing them herself by visiting them at home for several
weeks and discussed with them the timing of the transfer in
relation to their own perception of their readiness for it,
before actually instigating it. When the moment came for
her to withdraw Mr and Mrs Harrison were able to see this
primarily as a sign of improvement in their situation and
their ability to manage rather than feeling let down.

THE CASE OF PAULINE SMITH

Crohn's disease

Named after the physician who first described its features
and course, this disease causes abdominal pain, with weakness, weight loss and sometimes diarrhoea in relatively
young people. It is a rare disease, but it does serve as a
good example of a medical condition about which little is
known - for instance, its cause is obscure. Although the
pathological changes which predominate in the small bowel
are inflammatory, no infective agent has been consistently
isolated. In the absence of evidence pointing in another
direction, psychological causes are likely to be attributed,
but there is no firm basis for such a belief.
   Where the cause of a disease is not known, specific treatment is impossible (in the sense that penicillin is specific
treatment for a streptococcal infection, because it destroys
the main cause). The natural course of Crohn's disease is
to persist, but with small remissions of symptoms; symptoms are likely to occur in four out of every five years, but
fewer than 10 per cent of patients die of the disease.
   Treatment is basically a matter of relieving symptoms
such as pain or diarrhoea and of replacing deficits of

nutrition by a high calorie diet, protein supplements and
correction of anaemia. Acute episodes respond to cortisone derivatives, but in the long run the use of this powerful agent may reduce the chance of survival. The removal
of defective segments of bowel by surgery is an important
measure which brings real benefit and may sometimes bring
the disease process to an end. Where the area affected by
the disease necessitates the removal of a large part of the
intestines, an artificial opening into the bowel - ileostomy -
may be necessary. The effects of this procedure are both
distressing and disabling for many people.

Referral and medical situation

Pauline, who was 23 years old, was referred to the social
worker by her general practitioner for help with adjustment
to her chronic illness. She had suffered since the age of
19 from Crohn's disease and had undergone surgery two
years previously. Since then her health had been fluctuating - there were periods when she was able to lead a normal
life, whilst at other times her symptoms of anorexia,
diarrhoea and vomiting returned, leading to considerable
weight loss and general emaciation. Pauline's doctor
thought that her personality and social circumstances played
an important part in determining how well or unwell she was
and he therefore hoped that regular contacts with a social
worker over a period of time might help to stabilise her
condition.

Social work with Pauline Smith

Pauline came from a family of six children. She had an
elder married brother and two elder sisters - one married
and one, an unsupported mother, with a boy under five.
Her younger brother and sister were still at school and
living at home with the parents.
  Pauline had left home at 17 and for a time shared a flat
with a friend. She was very happy there, enjoying an
active social life and an interesting job. However, when
she became ill, she moved back into the family home at her
parents' invitation. Her relationships with her parents
were reasonably good, but they had few common interests.
Both did shift work - father working at night and mother

during the day, so there was little opportunity for them to spend much time together as a family. Pauline described her parents as hard working and anxious to better themselves materially. They had always provided well for their children.

At the time of referral Pauline had a job with the Gas Board as a clerk, earning good money and with short hours and little travelling to do. This job was kept open for her during her periods of sickness, but because of computerisation of accounts, her work had lately become rather boring and she was hoping to be redeployed within the company.

After a few interviews, the social worker assessed Pauline's difficulties along the following lines:

Pauline was a girl in late adolescence whose life has been radically affected by the onset of a chronic and incurable illness at a particularly vulnerable age. At a crucial stage in establishing her own identity as a person she had had to return to the family home, undergo surgery and experience a range of painful and depressing symptoms. These caused her to lose a lot of weight and changed her appearance considerably. On the whole, she was remarkably well able to cope with all these troubles, making the best of life when symptom-free and accepting depression as the natural consequence of her periods of vomiting and of pain. She seemed an intelligent and thoughtful girl, able to respond to help in developing insights into the personal and familial mechanisms influencing her feelings and behaviour. Unfortunately, at one stage, when she was first diagnosed as suffering from Crohn's disease, one of her doctors had rather ineptly discussed the meaning of psychosomatic illness with her in terms which made her think of it as something under a person's conscious control. Since then she has tended to blame herself for every recurrence of her symptoms.

Pauline had a basically positive outlook on life and wanted to be happy and successful. She found it difficult, however, to plan ahead or to make changes because of the constraints of her condition. She was entrenched in the family home and in a boring job, feeling moderately content over the former and unable to do much about the latter. She hoped to be redeployed in the near future but knew she would be unable to take the job of a showroom assistant, her preference, because it would be too taxing for her and she could not guarantee a good enough work attendance.

She did have a boyfriend whom she had been seeing for

about two years. She had always had ambivalent feelings towards him, however, and had recently terminated the relationship. She said she preferred to be friendly with a group of people and felt afraid of individual relationships. She was currently mixing with a group of boys who appeared to accept her as a companion; but she was highly critical of their attitudes towards their individual girl friends and felt this confirmed her reservations about personal involvement. She had no close girl friends.

A major source of difficulty for Pauline was the acceptance of her changed body image. Appearance and dress were very important to her and this led her at times to feeling very depressed about being so thin and shapeless and unable to wear fashionable clothes. She considered that her head was noticeably too large for her body.

Given all the circumstances, she was able for much of the time to cope well with her situation and was showing a sensible and a mature attitude towards it. However, when her symptoms became more severe, she got depressed and then entertained a lot of doubts about her future. She also worried about the extent of her own responsibility for what she regarded as her psychosomatic illness. She sometimes went as far in this as to question her sanity, maintaining that, 'no sane person would bring such symptoms upon themselves deliberately'.

In the course of regular weekly interviews over a period of six months, Pauline gradually came to trust the social worker and to use her for clarifying some of her confusions about herself, her family, and her illness. She seemed to have realised quickly the potential value of sharing her thoughts and feelings with an impartial, sympathetic outsider and made very good use of her time with the social worker. She readily acknowledged her loneliness and not having anyone in whom she could confide.

Her feelings towards the hospital doctors were very ambivalent and although she had a good relationship with her general practitioner, she did not feel she could discuss 'personal' matters with him. The interviews with Pauline were more orderly and structured than is often the case and this reflected partly her commitment to 'sorting things out' and partly her intelligence and her general sense of purpose. In different interviews specific aspects of her life were considered and it was clear that a good deal of 'homework' went on in Pauline's mind following and in between them.

Her relationship with her family was one of the themes
considered. Pauline came to realise that in many ways
different members of the family had depended on her as if
hers were a parental role and that she had encouraged this
dependency herself in the past. Consequently, when she
became ill and her own need for care and dependence
increased, her parents and her siblings found it difficult to
adjust to the changed situation and could only help by responding to her needs on a crisis basis rather than in a more
sustained manner. This realisation considerably eased
her ambivalence towards her family.

Much work went into helping Pauline adopt a more realistic and accepting attitude towards her illness and the extent
of her control over it. As she came to realise that she had
been given both conflicting and misleading information about
it in the past, she was able to seek a fuller and a less sim-
plistic explanation from her doctors about the diagnosis
and prognosis. In sharing it with the social worker she
was enabled to develop a more serene, less fatalistic, view
of the relationship between her personality and her illness.

The third main topic of Pauline's discussions with the
social worker was her personal and sexual identity. This
began with her needing a good deal of reassurance about her
inability as yet to feel at ease in the company of one young
man rather than a group, and also about her unwillingness
to become just another of the girls about whom the boys
talked with less than respect. It was very important for
her to have her high standards for herself acknowledged
and supported by the social worker. She was also helped
to look more objectively at her relationship with the ex-
boyfriend and see how her ambivalence towards him had
caused her to be excessively generous towards him. Her
accompanying inability to show dependence on him had
reinforced in him those characteristics which caused her
hurt and disappointment.

As a result of her thinking about her relationships with
her family and her boyfriend, Pauline recognised that there
was a certain common pattern to them all, derived largely
from her own difficulties in relinquishing control. She
seemed able to make use of this insight not only for intellectual gain but also, more importantly, in relation to her
emotional life. She became visibly more relaxed and more
outgoing.

The situation was considerably helped by Pauline's
employers offering her a different job (in the public

relations department) which she found both interesting and
challenging.

At the time of termination of the social worker's contacts
with Pauline (which was achieved by mutual consent) she
was both relatively symptom-free and much more comfortable in her living generally.

COMMENTARY

In the case of Mr Harrison, the social worker played an
important part in interpreting the problems of both the patient
and his wife to the medical and nursing staff of the hospital.
This in turn enhanced their tolerance of what they saw as
demanding and irrational behaviour by the couple.

It could be argued that there should be no need for such a
function by a social worker, because doctors and nurses
ought to be able themselves to understand and respond
appropriately to difficult behaviour. This, however, would
be taking an extreme idealistic view. It is better to realise
that there is a difference in the relationship to sick people
of doctors and nurses, and social workers. The ultimate
threat of death or serious disability causes patients to
invest doctors, in particular, with powers which are almost
magical; this leads them to feel dependent, which in turn
breeds ambivalence towards these omnipotent figures at
whose mercy they feel themselves to be. It is easier for
social workers than for doctors and nurses to avoid being
engulfed by these feelings, because they do not tend patients
physically.

It is therefore therapeutic for many patients to acknowledge within the safety of a relationship with a non-medical
person, yet one having a formal role, that they both fear
and resent their doctors as well as trusting them and feeling
grateful. From the doctor's point of view, provided he can
look upon the social worker as a dependable and a loyal
colleague, it helps his task of caring for the patient if he is
freed from some of the burden of exclusive or excessive
involvement in a patient's feelings about his own condition
and those who attend to it.

Another common problem illustrated by the Harrison case
is the effect on a marriage of role changes brought about by
illness of one partner. The degree of threat generated by
this depends on a number of factors of which the seriousness of the medical condition, the extent of the role change

it necessitates, and the personalities of the individuals involved, are particularly important. It calls for exceptional maturity, security and adaptability on the part of all marital partners to have to reverse their complementary roles suddenly and radically, when these have evolved over many years of mutual adjustment. In this respect, the social worker has a prima facie contribution to make, drawing on her general knowledge of human behaviour, marital interaction, and her skills in marital therapy, within the broader context of social work.

In Pauline's case the focus of the social work was on Pauline herself. It involved two separate though inter-related aspects: helping her to come to terms with her illness and promoting the growth of her personal identity.

Her difficulties in seeing her illness as psychosomatic reflect to some extent a more general problem with regard to the exact meaning and implications of this term. At least three different usages can be identified.

The first, which is part of the armoury of some organically minded doctors, is almost as a term of abuse. A patient labelled as suffering from 'psychosomatic symptoms' is one who has failed to produce a 'respectable' organic reason for these. In consequence, the symptoms are not accepted as medically genuine, with an implication of fraudulent motivation in having produced them.

The second usage refers to the body-mind interaction which occurs in all illness. In that sense, all illness is psychosomatic, but such a broad definition is of a limited use except as a reminder that a purely organic approach to ill health is insufficient.

The third and the most usual way in which the term 'psychosomatic' is used is in respect of certain particular diseases in which psychological conflict and stress are thought to be major causative factors. There is, however, little agreement within the medical profession as to which diseases should be included in this category, or what are the specific psychological causes underlying particular psychomatic conditions.

It is not altogether surprising therefore that Pauline was given an oversimplified (and distorted) picture of her illness by one of her doctors, or that she felt stigmatised by it. A more comfortable attitude towards the reality of her chronic ill health was clearly conditional on first shedding the burden of guilt and personal responsibility which had unwittingly been imposed upon her.

In many cases the nature of a person's illness would have
been made clearer by the doctor. People vary however in
who they choose to confide in, and Pauline found it easier to
discuss her 'personal' matters with the social worker. In
addition there is the important fact of differing levels of
comprehension. This means that a piece of medical information conveyed in the emotive setting of a medical consultation may need to be reflected upon and further considered
after an interval with the help of someone in a less emotionally fraught context. The fact that social workers, when
dealing with people who have health problems, spend a considerable amount of time discussing medical diagnosis and
its implications is usually not a reflection of the failure of
these clients' doctors to impart relevant knowledge. It is
rather an indication of people's difficulty in hearing painful
or anxiety-provoking messages and their need to go over
important facts at a later date and in the light of other
aspects of their lives.

Pauline's difficulties in establishing a personal and a
sexual identity could have justified social-work intervention without the further complication of her illness. She
felt responsible for her family, but they did not reciprocate
enough in accepting her needs. The problem was further
aggravated by her lack of an adult figure whom she could
use as a sounding board and a source of support in the face
of her various uncertainties and conflicts. Whether or not
she would have found her way to a social worker without the
medical referral is a matter for speculation.

Given the combination of her adolescent stresses and her
serious illness, there is no doubt as to the appropriateness
of Pauline's referral by her general practitioner.
Pauline's contacts with the social worker were clearly of
considerable help and value to her.

At a time when certain aspects of 'traditional' social work
practice are questioned by the exponents of 'radicalism', it
is interesting to note the constructive use of 'insight promotion' - the most frequently maligned of the social work
approaches. It was justified here not only by Pauline's
own thirst for greater self-knowledge but also by the
obvious need to help her develop as a mature person, able
to cope with a chronic and disabling disease.

The appropriateness of this approach in this case serves
to demonstrate the importance of a careful assessment of the
problems and needs of individual clients before any valid
decisions can be taken about preferred ways of helping them.

Therefore, good social work with sick people, as illustrated by these two cases, like good social work with any
type of client, calls for a sound general base of knowledge,
and skill in assessment and an ability to select and practise
appropriate intervention.

It is for this reason that we do not suggest any further
reading at the end of this chapter. To do so would have
entailed listing a large number of general texts on social-
work practice which, we must assume, are already familiar
to our social-work readers.

Chapter 4

Health in relation to age

INTRODUCTION

The significance of age as a factor in human life and an influence on health is obvious, yet easily overlooked.

It is seen most clearly in physiological changes: the nature and extent of body growth and the changes in body tissues and in their functioning. One only needs to think of the difference in physique between a 3-year-old child and one aged 12, or of the amount of food required by a young adult male and an old lady of 80, to appreciate the influence of physiology in all the age groups. The many differences in body metabolism which are linked with age help to determine both what constitutes an appropriate mode of living for people of different ages and what causes pathological states.

However, 'man cannot live by bread alone'. There are other factors besides purely physiological ones which affect health differently at different ages. Thus, what constitutes personal fulfilment and appropriate social status will vary with the age of the person concerned. What is considered appropriate dependence or healthy ambition also varies with age, and this too can affect health.

The various risks and stresses to which an individual is exposed are greatly influenced by his age. The number of children who die from accidents at home or who are killed on the roads is greatly in excess of deaths from disease. Certain forms of physical abuse (or 'battering') are a danger to which young children are particularly exposed. Anxiety states, with or without physical symptoms, are particularly prevalent in middle age, which is the period of

life in our culture when the 'fight for survival' in terms of
rivalry and competition is at its most acute.   A sense of
psychological void and lack of purpose, derived from the
absence of valued social roles, is a common feature of old
age.
   In this chapter we try to look at some of the many features
of health and disease which are related to particular age
groups and which have particular relevance for social work.
Readers must appreciate, however, that the discussion is
limited to those aspects which have the most direct relevance to health.   It must not therefore be seen as a substitute for a full study of human development throughout life.
A real grasp of the different health characteristics of the
'seven ages of man' depends on a sound understanding of all
the main features of these 'ages'.   It is for this reason
that we include under our suggestions for further reading
several titles concerned with a broader area of knowledge
than the more specific concerns of this chapter.
   For the purposes of our discussion we have divided the
natural continuity of a lifetime into sections on infants and
young children, aged 0-5; older children, aged 6-11;
adolescents, aged 12-20; young adults, 21-35; middle-aged
persons, aged 36-64; and old people, 65 onwards.

INFANTS AND YOUNG CHILDREN (AGE GROUP 0-5
YEARS)

It is customary and useful to divide this period of life for
medical purposes into three parts: the first month or neonatal period, the first year, the years from 1-5.   There
are medical problems peculiar to the neonatal month and
others which seldom arise after the first year.
   Throughout these five years disease and health have to
be considered against the background of rapid development
physically, intellectually, emotionally and socially.   It is
the rapidity of change in all these aspects of life that makes
the theme of development more important than with any subsequent age group.

The neonatal month

The miraculous way in which the vast majority of babies
survive the stress of being born and of the change to a

totally different environment is perhaps too readily taken
for granted. The change includes fundamentally different
ways of taking food and of getting oxygen. The mouth, the
intestines and the lungs are being used for the first time.

Normally born after being surrounded for forty weeks in
the uterus by fluid and obtaining every need through the
contact of the placenta with the mother's circulation, babies
can survive if born as early as thirty-two weeks after conception (and even earlier at times due to the various advances in the premature baby unit technology). At this time
they might weigh 1-2 lb, instead of the normal range in
weight of 5-9 lb. These premature babies are unlikely to
survive unless they are kept in an incubator with special
methods of feeding and constant surveillance.

Disease in the first month is of four sorts. Rarely it
may have started within the uterus, as with haemolytic disease of the newborn, where there has been an incompatibil-
ity between the blood of the baby and that of the mother,
resulting in the baby being jaundiced at birth. Next it may
be due to one of the many forms of congenital defect – failure
in normal development of the foetus. The commonest and
most important of these congenital defects are those affecting the heart, the hip joints, the brain, or the spinal cord.
A third type of disease may be due to birth injury because
of difficult labour or delay in starting to breathe. Finally,
infections can develop after birth, notably in the skin, the
lungs and the urinary tract.

Most of these problems will be identified while the baby
is still in hospital. Those that are transient have little
importance to most social workers, but many congenital
defects are permanent. According to their nature and
severity they demand varying degrees of acceptance and
adjustment from parents. An extreme example is a baby
born with hydrocephalus, spina bifida and meningocele,
when the chances of survival are remote. Congenital dis-
location of the hip and abnormalities of the heart mean that
major surgical intervention has to be faced with all the
accompanying stresses. We discuss some of the problems
of handicapped children and their parents more fully later
in this chapter.

The first year

After the first month, disease in the first year follows the general pattern for the whole age group 0-5, but certain problems deserve special mention. Teething usually starts at 4-6 months and accounts for a quantity of minor misery for children and parents, including loss of sleep. Eczema may start at this age in pre-disposed children; for most it will be a minor problem, but for some it may involve a large area of the skin and herald the later development of asthma. The combination of eczema and asthma can become a major and long-lasting problem for children and their parents.

The occurrence of convulsions when a feverish illness starts is fairly common under the age of 3. It only rarely heralds a more permanent tendency to fits, but it is a frightening experience for parents when it occurs.

Infections are important under the age of 1 because a baby's resistance may be relatively weak. Particularly important are gastro-enteritis (diarrhoea and vomiting, which can lead rapidly to a serious state of fluid depletion), skin infections, and whooping cough (complicated at this age by secondary infections in the lung and leading occasionally to permanent damage to lung tissue). Urinary infections are important, partly because they are difficult to recognise as reasons for a feverish illness, and partly because they may lead to damage to the kidneys. They are particularly likely to occur when there is already some congenital defect in the anatomy of the urinary tract.

Immunisation against certain infectious diseases starts in the first year. This represents the most sure and dramatic success in preventive medicine, in contributing to the virtual disappearance of smallpox, diphtheria and poliomyelitis, and the control of whooping cough, tetanus and measles.

The principle of immunisation is to stimulate the natural defences of the body by giving a small and harmless dose of the infection in question, whether it be viral or bacterial. The technical problem is to derive from the active germ a substance which will stimulate lasting immunity without precipitating a significant or dangerous reaction.

The present controversy over immunisation against whooping cough arises because such dangerous reactions have actually occurred in a very small number of previously healthy infants, and some of these have left lasting damage. This is, of course, a tragedy, but whooping cough itself,

if it occurs in the first year of life, can have equally disas-
trous consequences in a small number of cases. Public
health policy becomes therefore a matter of accurate statistics and the balancing of risks. Most careful work at the
national level has led to the conclusion that the risks of
whooping cough outweigh those of immunisation and that this
should therefore continue. Such general policy does not,
however, resolve completely the problem for individual
parents who still have to make their decision in the light of
the knowledge that either course of action may result in
brain damage to their child.

Both food refusal and failure to sleep are very common
difficulties in the first year. They are usually transient
and should be assumed to be so unless time proves them to
be otherwise. They may stem from temporary causes within
the child, even from unsuspected illness, but it is important
to remember that there are great temperamental differences
between babies. Alternatively, such problems may stem
from a difficulty in the relationship to one or other parent,
which ever is more involved in the care of the infant, or
they may reflect difficulties in the parental relationship.
The important point to note is that all behavioural problems
in young children require careful observation and thorough
discussion with the parents if their cause in a particular
instance is to be understood. As already implied, such
understanding may well lead to help being focused on the
parents' needs for support in meeting the demands of
parenthood.

The subject of the nature of the needs of small children is
one on which opinions are often substituted for refutable
evidence and reliable knowledge. There is, however,
sufficient agreement on certain basic matters which are best
summed up by the popular term 'loving care'. On the physical side this means cleanliness, suitable food and adequate
sleep. On the psychological and social side, the following
statement by Dr Catriona Hood, an authority on infant care,
provides a good indication of the important criteria:
'Continuity of care in a loving, familiar and stable environment where the child is valued for his uniqueness.'

1 to 5 years

Regular developmental checks are the key to medical,
surgical, educational and social help for children with

health defects. Their importance was reiterated recently
by the Committee on Child Health Services. (1)
 Disease in the years 1-5 consists chiefly of infections:
mumps, measles, German measles and chickenpox. Infection of the respiratory tract, particularly the nose, throat
and ears, is especially common when children come into
contact with others outside their home and before they have
had time to develop the relative immunity which protects
their elders. Infections of tonsils and adenoids, with
resulting enlargement of both, are particularly liable to
afflict this age group.
 Infections of the middle ear are a common secondary
event in the wake of tonsillitis, colds, or influenza. In
the past otitis media had in its turn important complications:
perforated eardrum, chronic discharging ear infections,
mastoid infections, even meningitis and brain abscess. It
is one of the most striking benefits of antibiotic treatment
that these complications are now very rare. Other sites
for infections in the 1-5-year-olds are the bronchial tubes,
the lungs, the urinary tract and the skin.
 Abdominal pain is a common health problem in this age
group. For most parents 'tummy pain' in a child raises
the fear of acute appendicitis. For a child it is very likely
to be a way of indicating a pain which has its origins somewhere else in the body. To the doctor it provides an important and sometimes a difficult diagnostic challenge.
 Appendicitis and most other abdominal conditions in
children which require the help of a surgeon are likely to
be acute episodes, increasing in severity within hours.
They are far less common than other less serious causes of
abdominal pain, such as bowel colic from eating too fast or
too much or something unsuitable, or the pain which accompanies infections of the throat and is attributable to the
involvement of lymph glands in the abdomen. (It is rare for
small children with tonsillitis to complain of their throat;
they are more likely to mention their head or stomach.)
Gastro-enteritis is another common cause of abdominal pain.
It is an infection of the bowel, due to a variety of agents,
which usually reveals itself by pain accompanied by both
vomiting and diarrhoea. Urinary infections can also cause
abdominal pain, although they are less obvious and are
detectable only with the help of a bacteriological culture of
the urine. All these forms of disorder tend to be sudden,
to last a day or two and to be accompanied by obvious fever.
 Recurrent abdominal pain, lasting an hour or two and

coming and going for weeks or months, presents a different
type of problem. It needs careful observation and analysis
which often results in clues relating it to emotional distress
originating either at home or at school. This association
between abdominal pain and emotional factors is one illustration of the extent to which in young children the body acts
as a major vehicle for expressing such feeling states as
unhappiness and anxiety. An important factor in this is
young children's limited ability to articulate their emotional
problem verbally.

OLDER CHILDREN (AGE GROUP 6-11)

Physical diseases occur less frequently in this age group
than in younger children. Immunity to infections is greater
than before the age of 5, although they are still the most
important cause of ill health. However, liability to accidents increases with increasing mobility and zest for
adventure.
  Medical examination of school children is directed at continuing to detect defects of sight and hearing which could
explain learning difficulties and the more subtle defects of
intelligence, emotional and social development which can
lead to long-term handicap and yet are frequently amenable
to medical, educational or social help.
  The problem of enuresis deserves special mention. If a
child is unable to control urination by the age of 5, this is
usually regarded as abnormal. In a few instances, such
failure may have as its cause a congenital anomaly somewhere in the urinary tract, or an infection, or both. More
commonly, however, no identifiable physical cause exists.
A relationship between enuresis and emotional difficulties
can often be established, especially in those instances
where a child starts to wet again after a period of full control. It is a mistake to assume, however, that in the
absence of a physical explanation enuresis is always due to
emotional distress. It may be the result of failure in
habit formation or of a particularly slow development in this
respect.
  Many cases of enuresis become resolved spontaneously.
Some respond to the interest taken when the problem is
treated as medical and after consultation has taken place.
The use of a bell which rings directly wetting in bed occurs
is surprisingly successful in some instances. Enuresis

provides yet another example of what is still very common
in medical practice, namely the need to be involved and to
act where there is no clear understanding about cause and
little agreement about management. The latter does include,
in appropriate cases, both psychotherapeutic and behavioural
measures; doctors, and psychologists and social workers
all may have an important contribution to make.

The child aged 6-11 is usually relatively healthy from the
physical point of view, but this is not necessarily the case
with regard to emotional health. Various unresolved conflicts from the early stages of the relationship between the
child and his parents may come to the fore and manifest
themselves in the form of behavioural symptoms. These
include, in addition to enuresis already mentioned, soiling,
excessively aggressive behaviour, learning difficulties and
uncontrollable jealousy of a sibling. Equally, various
somatic symptoms without a primary or a demonstrable
physical cause may occur. Their prevalence is the reason
why it is during this age period that most referrals to child
guidance clinics occur.

A good illustration of the close connection between behavioural difficulties in a child and the nature of his family
relationships is provided by the problem of school refusal.
Some children find it so difficult to face up to having to go
to school that they will become acutely ill rather than respond to the requirements of adults in this respect. There
is now considerable evidence that underlying many instances
of school refusal (which needs to be distinguished from
truanting) are difficulties on the part of the parent (usually
the mother) in letting go of the child. The mother's own
needs are such that she conveys to the child a 'double-bind'
message: overtly, she tells him to go to school, but on a
less conscious level she communicates to him her desperate
need of him and his company. In these circumstances
attendance at school would entail for the child a betrayal of
his parent and the resulting guilt would be overwhelming.
In addition, mother's invitation' to him to stay at home has
usually an element of personal gratification for him, and so he
readily colludes with her.

As has already been stressed, help to children with
behavioural problems involves helping their parents as well.
If problems are spotted at an early enough stage, help to
parents may be sufficient to remove the symptoms in the
child. This possibility provides an important reason why
the availability of social workers in strategic positions,

such as with general medical practices or attached to
schools, is important as a means of promoting health in
children.

Death in childhood

For every thousand children born in 1974 sixteen died during
the first year of life.   The comparable number in 1971 was
seventeen, in 1951 thirty, in 1931 sixty-six and in 1911
one hundred and thirty.
   The cause of this improvement in infantile mortality must
be attributed at least as much to changes in nutrition, housing, sanitation and parental understanding as to advances in
the practice of medicine.   The trend is similar for all
countries of comparable development, but in recent years
this country has dropped in rank when compared with
others, including Sweden, the Netherlands, France, Swit-
zerland and Japan.
   The failure on the part of Britain to keep pace with other
developed countries in making birth and the first months of
life less hazardous is a matter for serious concern.   Both
the 'Report of Child Health Services' (2) and the more
recent Report on 'Inequalities in Health' (3) provide evidence of considerable discrepanices in the rates of still-
births, neonatal deaths and infant deaths as between the
different social classes.   Thus, according to the former
report:
   A child born into the family of a semi-skilled or unskilled
   worker is twice as likely to die between the end of the
   first month and the end of the first year of life (when
   environment and other related factors tell most strongly)
   as a child born to parents in social classes I and II.
   Twice as many children of unskilled workers die in the
   first month of life as children of professional workers
   and the gap between the social classes in this respect
   has been widening steadily for 25 years.   Two and a half
   times more children die in classes IV and V than in
   classes I and II of certain infectious diseases.   Children still die in our life time for nineteenth century
   reasons (p. 6).
   In addition to the social class factor, considerable disadvantages both at birth and in early childhood are related
to young age of the mothers, their failure to use ante-
natal services and to heavy smoking and alcohol consumption

during pregnancy.   Infants of mothers in these groups are
more likely to have been born prematurely and to have had
a low birthweight.
    After the first year of life the risk of death becomes much
less, as shown in Table 4.1 taken from the 'Report of the
Committee on Child Health Services' (p. 47):

TABLE 4.1 Number of deaths at different ages in childhood
and adolescence in England and Wales in 1974

First year	10,459
Years 1-4	1,922
Years 5-9	1,225
Years 10-14	1,091
Years 15-19	2,212

    'Cot deaths' - deaths occurring suddenly and unexpectedly
- have been a growing cause of concern in recent years not
least because they are a mystery.   They are certainly not
derived from a single cause.   In a third of them there is
known disease capable of explaining the death; in the
remainder, there is evidence of disturbed growth, but not
of disease.   The death of a truly well child is rare.
Nevertheless the sudden nature of these deaths (half of
which occur at home) comes as a great shock to parents and
the family doctor, especially as a quarter appear, in retro-
spect, to have been avoidable.   According to one authority:
    The main factors leading to death are the inability of
    parents to recognise the importance of symptoms, or to
    avail themselves of the Health Service; the amount of
    drive and persistence required to obtain general practice
    services in some areas; and the failure of some practi-
    tioners to recognise severely ill children. (4)
The 'Report of the Committee on Child Health Services'
states that (p. 42):
    Accidents are the principal cause of death between 1 and
    15 years and although rates in the younger age groups
    have declined, for the 15-19s they are significantly
    higher than they were 20 years ago....   The extent of
    non-fatal accidents is unknown and the professional time
    spent in treating them unmeasured.   In 1972 141,000
    children were admitted to hospital with accidental injuries

and 1,800 died.... The home is more dangerous than the roads, especially with limited space and with limited parental understanding.

Handicaps in children

The Committee on Child Health Services defines handicap as: 'a disability which, for a substantial period or permanently, retards, distorts or otherwise adversely affects normal growth, development or adjustment in life' (p. 45).
    The incidence and prevalence of handicaps in children is frequently underestimated. According to one widely quoted study, (5) one child in every seven was found to be handicapped in some way. Table 4.2, taken from that study, shows the prevalence of the four major handicapping conditions among 9-11-year-old children:

TABLE 4.2

Condition*	Physical handicap	Intellectual handicap	Educational backwardness	Psychological** disorder
Total with each handicap (%)	2.7	2.6	7.9	6.8

  * Moderate and severe cases only.
 ** Estimate.

    The Committee on Child Health Services, commenting on these figures have said this (pp. 45-6):
    In 1973, 2,151 children under 15 years were registered as blind or partially sighted, and 4,330 as deaf or partially deaf. Since diagnosis and notification are not uniform throughout the country, these figures are probably an underestimate.... Among the physically handicapped the most familiar group are those with the restricted movement and abnormal posture of cerebral palsy. The severe forms make immense demands on the child, parents, therapists, doctors, social workers, teachers and eventually on the employment service.
    The prevalence of mildly handicapped children is approximately $2\frac{1}{2}$ per cent of the child population. These children

suffer largely from intellectual retardation and are in consequence 'slow learners'. A large proportion of them
come from Social Class V. Some who suffer from additional handicaps, such as some form of pathology of the
central nervous system, need expert medical services,
but the needs of the majority are best met by appropriate
educational and social provision.

The situation is very different with regard to those
children who suffer from severe mental handicap. The
degree of their intellectual retardation is such that they
need specialised services. The 'Report of the Committee
on Child Health Services' estimates that (p. 241): 'about 4
children in every 1,000 who survive to adolescence are
severely retarded'. The 'Report' quotes the Kushlick
Survey (6) to provide data regarding the prevalence of different types of mental handicap (p. 241).

Among those aged 15-19 yrs, 28% suffered from Down's
syndrome (mongolism), 10% had cerebral palsy (and three
fifths of these were unable to walk) and 12.5% suffered
from epilepsy. Among the younger children (aged 0-5)
16% were non-ambulant, 17% had a severe behaviour disorder and 10% were incontinent. The remainder (two-
thirds of the total number) were continent, ambulant and
had no severe behaviour problem.

The contribution of social work to the health care of children

An important general characteristic of this contribution,
especially in relation to very young children, is that it is
focused on helping the children's parents. The younger the
child, the more completely he is dependent for his very survival, as well as for his welfare and health, on his immediate environment; his parents usually constitute that
environment.

It is an obvious fact that a newly born infant is at a considerable disadvantage if there are any major defects in his
parents' ability to meet his massive needs for dependence.
Absence of one of the parents is one such disadvantage.
Although the stigma of unmarried motherhood is now much
less than it was in Victorian England, to many a single girl
and her family the arrival of a baby still constitutes tangible
evidence of her having behaved in a way which is socially
disapproved. This, coupled with financial, housing and
other problems which are a frequent feature of unmarried

motherhood, does mean that the baby is viewed with mixed feelings - a source of hardship and embarrassment as well as an object of love. Many single girls can keep their babies only at a considerable cost to both, and yet their ambivalent feelings make it extremely hard for them to reach a firm decision regarding the baby's future without undue delay.

Although there are some differences in interpretation and emphasis (as, for example, between Rutter (7) and Freud et al. (8)), most authorities on child welfare agree that the stability and consistency of love takes precedence over the 'blood bond' as far as the needs of young children are concerned. This means that adoption at as early an age as possible is a far more satisfactory alternative for a child than his being brought up in an atmosphere of excessive ambivalence or by an ever-changing series of people. Social workers therefore have an important part to play in helping unmarried mothers with their confused feelings and with reaching a responsible decision for their child's future welfare. This is frequently a very painful one to make - assisting with it calls for considerable knowledge of human personality as well as skill in counselling.

Handicapped children

An important and yet currently neglected area of social work is in relation of physically and mentally handicapped children.

Having a handicapped child is a disappointment and sorrow to parents (see, for example, Olshansky (9)). It constitutes the loss of the hopes and ambitions they have had for the child, and of their own self-esteem, resulting from the failure to produce a normal and a 'whole' child. Such an experience of loss, and the grief which accompanies it, can and often does lead to extreme attitudes towards the child which are not in his long-term interests and some of which can be very damaging to him. The two most common are an outright rejection or an over-protectiveness.

Given the nature and the extent of the difficulties facing the parents of a handicapped child, it is of the utmost importance that they should have ready access to appropriate forms of help from the moment of birth and throughout the crucial formative years. Social workers have a contribution to make during the whole of this period in ensuring maximum achievement on the part of the child in terms of both personal adjustment and social functioning.

It is now generally understood that, unless parents of a handicapped child can receive appropriate help with their feelings of shock and grief at the point when they first discover what has befallen them, they may fail to come to terms with reality. This will severely impede their ability to respond appropriately to the needs of the child. It is therefore important for social workers to see parents shortly after the news has been first broken to them and to keep in close touch with them during both the critical period of initial mourning and the later stage when realistic plans concerning the child's future need to be discussed. It is also important for social workers to be available to the family during further crucial stages in the development of the handicapped child, such as the beginning of schooling, changing schools and securing employment, where this is appropriate. This is because the transitions and crises in life present additional difficulties to families with a handicapped child and they can easily prove unmanageable without appropriate help and support.

Both practical help and emotional support are important in work with these families. There is evidence that the constant strain of looking after the child affects parents' health and that there is excessive illness in these families as a result. Therefore, anything which eases the task of looking after a severely handicapped child - an improved income, adaptations to the home, day-care facilities, breaks in the daily routine, being enabled to take a holiday - is of a paramount importance. So is a continuous relationship with a trusted person who can be used as a sounding board, a comforter, and a general source of support.

Unfortunately, coupled with the evidence of these needs is the fact that, like so many other professionals, doctors included, social workers give a low priority to work with handicapped children and their families. In his recently published book, Lansdown (10) includes the following quotation from Hewett (11):

There is one central theme which runs like a thread through the various sections of this report: briefly it is clear that the channels of communication between the parents themselves and those who have the responsibility of trying to help them are constricted and congested at very many different points (p. 16).

One reason for this reluctance to engage in work in this

area may be lack of confidence in their own knowledge and
skills. This factor was certainly revealed by Fox (12)
and it is possible that it is this which prompted the Committee on Child Health Services to recommend 'the development
of post-qualification training in the field of child handicap' (13) for social workers.

The common social needs of children

The influence on children's health, physical and emotional,
of parental attitudes and handling pinpoints the importance
of appropriate help, support and guidance being readily
available to parents, especially parents of first children.
As some of this can best be provided by social workers, a
strong case can be made that they should be an integral part
of both the obstetric and the paediatric services in hospitals, as well as being members of primary health-care
teams in the community.
    One group of parents who are generally regarded as
being particularly vulnerable are those whose infants are
born prematurely. In general terms parents of prematurely
born infants have certain similar reactions to those experienced by parents of handicapped children: they too feel
undermined in their role of procreation and parenthood and
they too feel apprehensive about their capacity to meet the
additional demands imposed by their baby's special needs,
e.g. feeding difficulties and susceptibility to infections.
There is often an initial problem in establishing a mother/
infant bond, especially if the baby has had to spend the first
few weeks of his life away from the mother in an incubator.
    The recommendations of the Committee on Child Health
Services for an integrated multi-disciplinary child health
service reflect an appreciation of the indivisibility of many
health problems from the social environment within which
the child is growing up. The evidence for this is to be
found in many studies, including the National Child Development Study (14) and that by Douglas. (15) These have
demonstrated beyond doubt that such factors as parental
attitudes towards child rearing, the father's occupation, the
family income, the nature of housing and of the physical
environment in general, exercise a crucial influence upon
the general well-being of children, including their physical
and psychological health. In view of this, teamwork by
doctors, social workers, nurses, health visitors, teachers

and others (not to mention the parents) seems to be a particularly important prerequisite to the provision of adequate
health care.   It was certainly evident from the discussion
above of the particular problems facing both 'abused' and
handicapped children that effective intervention calls for
multi-disciplinary collaboration of a very close kind.

A good deal of preventive work could also be achieved in
relation to school children if more social workers were
attached to schools and were in a position to spot the beginnings of difficulties.   Only too often referrals to Education
Welfare Officers (not all of whom have had social work
training), to social workers in Social Services Departments
or to probation officers, come when the problems have
become serious as in cases of prolonged non-attendance or
delinquency.   Given the importance of the school setting
to children, too many social workers show insufficient
appreciation of the need for interest and a close involvement
on their part in that area of childhood experience.

We already mentioned earlier in this chapter the contribution which social workers can make to the health and well-
being of some children in this age group in the context of
teamwork in child guidance clinics.   These clinics see some
of the more disturbed children whose behavioural and family
relationship problems have escalated and have become intractable.   Much of the social work in relation to these
problems is concerned with helping parents and with liaising
with others on behalf of the child to make his social environment more understanding and tolerant.   Social work in this
setting is greatly enriched by its collaboration with both
psychiatry and psychology (both clinical and educational) and
it is not surprising therefore that it can in turn offer specialist guidance and teaching to social workers in the generalist setting of local authority social services departments.

ADOLESCENTS (AGE GROUP 12-20)

'The period of adolescence is defined by development rather
than by age' ('Report of the Committee on Child Health Services', p. 163).   It is therefore arbitrary to relate adolescence too specifically to an age group and the main value of
this is statistical.   For example, as the same Report continues: 'At ages 10-15 there is within any group of boys and
girls a range of development from pre-puberty to complete
physical maturity' (p. 163).

Adolescence is a lengthy state of human development extending from puberty until the achievement of biological, psychological and social maturity. The advent of puberty varies in different individuals and the attainment of maturity in all these three areas (always a relative achievement only), does not conform to any specific age limit. Some adolescents become adults at 18 or even sooner, whilst with others this is delayed as late as 25 years. Given the extended nature of the adolescent period and the considerable individual differences in reaching maturity, it is important to avoid thinking of adolescence in static terms or of adolescents as a homogeneous group. On the contrary, their needs and problems must be seen as individually varied and constantly changing throughout the process of development towards self-responsibility.

Disease in adolescents

Apart from anorexia nervosa and the related condition of bulaemia in which gluttonous eating is followed by self-induced vomiting, there are very few physical disorders peculiar to this age group. Other diseases which may persist through childhood, such as tonsillitis, bronchitis, asthma or eczema, usually improve at puberty, if not earlier.

Such new disorders as arise at this age are usually associated with the beginnings of sexual life; they will be discussed in the next section on young adults. The subject of the control of childbirth is also discussed in that section.

In contrast to disease, the incidence of serious physical injury is quite high amongst adolescents. This is mostly due to road accidents and in 1973 these claimed the death of 1,100 young people between the ages of 15 and 19. This problem too will be considered in more detail in the section on young adults.

Habits of smoking tobacco, drinking alcohol and taking drugs usually start in this age group and these may rapidly become fixed for a lifetime. The evidence that cigarette-smoking has a profound influence on the incidence of several fatal diseases later in life is now generally accepted. In view of this it is particularly regrettable that so little attention is given to health education in schools on which the 'Report of the Committee on Child Health Services' puts great emphasis.

Emotional problems in adolescents

The changes which occur in the body at puberty call for considerable adaptation of the body image. The experience of
strong sexual urges by boys and the onset of menstruation in
girls, and the other central features of puberty, give rise
to various mental fantasies which often frighten and induce
guilt at a time when, as part of the emancipation from the
family, adolescents may feel alienated from their parents.
They are the last people with whom an adolescent feels able
to discuss and share worries. It is therefore particularly
important for doctors and social workers to be aware of the
frequency of these hidden anxieties in young people and to
be prepared to discuss them and provide reassurance.
This is often best offered in the form of factual explanation.
Opportunities occur frequently.

Because this is such a crucial formative period in life,
the quality and the appropriateness of the help offered to
adolescents with their personal problems will have far-
reaching effects for their future. This calls for particular
knowledge and skills on the part of both doctors and social
workers in the areas of differential diagnosis and a helping
relationship. Thus, for example, both masturbation and
homosexual practices are common behavioural manifestations in adolescence. They are frequently an adolescent's
response to the stresses he experiences during this developmental period and are often transitory. Owing to the
social taboos which surround such practices, however, they
are accompanied for the adolescent by considerable guilt
and not infrequently by forebodings of future punishments
which will befall him as a result of his wickedness. If
such guilt is not allayed, it may have lasting pathological
effects, especially in relation to married life. Doctors and
social workers have therefore an important role; they can
put their many encounters with adolescents to a good use by
helping them get these troubling matters into a healthy perspective.

Another important differentiation to be made concerns the
possible onset of juvenile schizophrenia. This needs to be
distinguished from such normal behavioural manifestations
of adolescence as sudden mood swings, asceticism or an
excessive preoccupation with concepts and ideas at the
expense of concrete reality. Depression is also not uncommon among adolescents. This is often an aspect of their
regret for the lost dependence of childhood and the right

response to it is therefore similar to that of any form of mourning: recognition of its validity, acceptance of its worth and a conveying of hope regarding the future.

Suicide by adolescents is not uncommon and is a major cause of death in this age group. The incidence of attempted suicide is particularly high and is thought to reflect both proneness to depressive moods and the extent of the need to draw attention to emotional plight. These facts call for an early recognition of that quality and degree of depression in an adolescent which transcends the normal developmental 'doldrums' and which makes him vulnerable to suicide.

The preoccupation of adolescents with their body image, which is such an integral part of the development of their sense of personal identity, coupled with their tendency to react by extremes, can result in various forms of fads and excesses. Thus a fear of obesity can lead to under-nourishment and distress over the appearance of acne may result in morbid isolation. These various forms of over-reaction to bodily change may need to be watched and responded to if they endanger health. They are however qualitatively different from anorexia nervosa, a serious condition occurring mainly in adolescent girls and thought by many authorities to reflect a basic inability on their part to come to terms with their sexuality. Although recovery after a long illness is the more usual outcome, refusal of all food by these patients can sometimes lead to death from starvation. The condition calls for prolonged and specialised treatment on an inpatient basis.

Experimentation of all kinds is a common feature of adolescence and its function can best be understood in the context of the adolescent's need to find his own unique way of living. Some forms of experimentation are, however, fraught with greater risks than others. These include sexual intercourse and drugs. The contracting of venereal disease is one of the more obvious hazards as is shown by the increased incidence of gonorrhea in young girls. Unwanted pregnancy is another obvious risk and this gives rise to an important ethical question regarding the advisability of providing contraception to adolescents, and in what circumstances. A great responsibility rests upon all those including doctors and social workers who have a part to play in assisting adolescents to find a mode of behaviour which will both fulfil their own needs and will reflect a sense of commitment and responsibility towards others.

YOUNG ADULTS (AGE GROUP 21-35)

Like older children and adolescents, young adults are relatively healthy. The important distinction from the previous
age groups is in the differing experience of men and women.
The incidence of disease in young women is noticeably
greater than in young men, although it does not reach the
levels afflicting small children and older people. Clearly
sexual intercourse, marriage and above all childbirth and
the strains of bringing up young children have a marked
influence on the health of women between 21 and 35 years.

For this reason the medical problems of men and women
will be treated separately in this section, but there are
certain important characteristics which cannot be separated
in this way, because they are essentially shared, and
because they form a background for any discussion of diseases, injuries or handicaps in either sex.

The control of childbirth

The prevention of childbirth through some form of contraception is an important concern for young people and one
which increasingly is not confined to married couples.
According to Schofield (16) sexual experience before marriage is now nearer to being the norm than an exception.
It does not necessarily follow that most young people are
promiscuous or that they divorce sexual intercourse from
love, but the availability of effective contraception has
helped to combine the search for a lasting relationship with
physical intercourse.

The choice of contraceptive method presents some problems, as no method is perfect. The arguments in favour of
'the pill' in one of its many varieties are firstly that it is
the surest method of preventing conception and secondly
that it is very convenient. The arguments against it are
that in a small percentage of women it causes clotting to
occur in leg veins and that it may slightly increase the
chance of cardiovascular disorders later in life. Suspicion that it increases the chance of developing cervical
cancer has not been confirmed. There is some evidence,
however, that the contraceptive pill encourages the development of cancer in the cavity of the uterus in women over the
age of 35, especially in those who smoke. In view of this,
it is generally thought better not to use this form of contraception after that age.

The intra-uterine device as a guard against pregnancy is not as reliable as 'the pill'. It may also give rise to heavy menstrual bleeding or cause infection in a minority of women and have to be removed. On the other hand, it is convenient and does not carry the long-term risks attaching to 'the pill'.

Before these methods became available about fifteen years ago, the best contraceptive device was the cap or diaphragm, inserted by the woman prior to intercourse and removed twelve hours afterwards. This carries no risks, but it is less reliable as a method of preventing childbirth and a majority of women now see it as inconvenient and cumbersome by comparison with the other methods.

The snag about the condom worn by the man as a contraceptive device is that it takes the control over conception away from the person who stands to lose most if the method fails. Its reliability is the same as that of the diaphragm and it is still a popular method.

The 'rhythm' or 'safe period' method of contraception depends on avoiding intercourse at those times in the month when conception is most likely. Its value would be greatly enhanced if these times could be reliably predicted and were confined to fewer days than seems in fact to be the case. However, research aimed at refining the method and making it more foolproof is continuing. The importance of this lies in the fact that the use of the 'rhythm' method is the only acceptable method to those who have religious or ethical objections to mechanical or chemical interference with the natural processes of copulation and procreation.

Childbirth is rare after 45 years of age, but it is not impossible to conceive even after 50 in the case of women who have an exceptionally late menopause. For this reason many women prefer to continue with some form of contraception until about the age of 50.

Marital problems

Marital problems are frequently the concern of social workers, but they are also an important cause of medical consultation, especially with general practitioners. They are not always presented openly and directly, but they will often be found to underlie symptoms which cannot be explained in terms of recognisable disease. To list the full range of such symptoms would be too big a task, because the physical manifestations of emotional disorders can occur in any part of the body. Perhaps the commonest are insomnia, headache of various kinds, abdominal symptoms and disorders of menstruation. It is usually not difficult to ascertain when such symptoms are accompanied by feelings of tension, tiredness, anxiety, or depression. Frequent consultations for a variety of symptoms are a common sign of underlying emotional problems.

Usually it is one partner who presents the problem, whether openly or in disguise; most commonly it is the wife, but, as we have already mentioned, physical or behavioural problems in children can also provide a cue to a stressful relationship between the parents.

There are certain times in a marriage when problems are especially liable to arise: within the first year, after the birth of the first child and when the children have grown up and left home. According to Dominian, (17) the peak period for divorce is in the first seven years of marriage, but separation, the really significant point, occurs most frequently in the first two years. It is also well established that marriages entered into before the age of 20 are more vulnerable than those that start later.

In a book which aims predominantly to help social workers in their understanding of medical problems, there is no scope for discussion of the various causes of marital break-up. Since, however, sexual difficulties are among these causes, a brief mention of some of them seems appropriate. A primary physical basis for such difficulties is found much less often than an emotional one. As Dominian has put it: 'The majority of persistently serious sexual complaints are the end result of personality conflicts manifesting themselves in this extremely sensitive area. Sexual dissatisfaction in turn aggravates the relationship, thus setting up a vicious circle which may end in marital breakdown.'

There may be initial difficulties which, if not properly handled at the outset, can result in persistent sexual problems. Thus, a woman's vaginal opening may be small and at intercourse she may become tense through actual pain or through fear of it; penetration then becomes difficult or even impossible. Clumsiness on the part of the male at the first intercourse can be another reason for a woman's apprehension, as may be her fear of becoming pregnant or losing control. A vicious circle can be set up in which fear increases muscular tension and resistance ('vaginismus'), so that each attempt at penetration becomes more painful. Husband and wife will both need help; the earlier this is sought and given the more likely it is to succeed - but it must be help which is informed and skilful.

The most common sexual failure in males is premature ejaculation with too early loss of erection. Tiredness and anxiety may start the problem, but more serious causes are those due to physical disorders such as diabetes mellitus or disease of the central nervous system. Sexual deviations, particularly homosexuality, may also play a part as well as certain characteristics in the personality.

Sexual failure is a complex area of medical experience, ill understood by many doctors. It requires both specialist knowledge and a special sensitivity in its management. Early identification and prompt help are very important. A social worker can play a useful role in this respect by being able to see the problem in the context of the couple's overall relationship and their general life circumstances.

Infertility

Failure to conceive within a year or two of unprotected intercourse does not necessarily mean infertility. Doctors are only too familiar with cases where conception has occurred shortly after a couple has sought consultation because of fear of infertility, or after adoption of a child has been undertaken. These facts highlight the importance of emotional factors in this type of problem.

The incidence of 'true' infertility in the population of reproductive age and desiring to have children is around 8 per cent of marriages. The causes are many and may relate to the male or female, or both - those connected with the female are most frequent. In many cases the cause cannot be ascertained within the limits of present knowledge and methods of investigation.

A simple reason for failure to conceive may be due to true intercourse with penetration not having taken place, or occurring only rarely. There may be no sperm or too few sperm in the semen, and in addition to this another possible cause of infertility in the male is the absence of ejaculation, or ejaculation being premature and no semen being therefore deposited in the vagina. In some women the Fallopian tubes may be blocked through a past infection, making it impossible for ova to reach the uterus for implantation. There may also be a failure to ovulate, whether or not associated with an absence of menstruation. A proportion of these conditions are treatable, but some cause permanent and irreversible infertility.

There is evidence that genetic factors play a part in determining the degree of fertility. Some families appear to have a relatively low conception rate: for instance, a woman who is an only child is said to have only a 60 per cent chance of conceiving and a 34 per cent chance of having more than one child.

Venereal disease

The important diseases transmitted through sexual intercourse are syphilis, gonorrhoea and non-specific urethritis. Trichomonad and monilial (thrush) infections are common, but not serious in their effect on health.

The incidence of the important venereal diseases in this country was very high immediately after the last war, but dropped so much when the antibiotics were first used to treat them that their disappearance was forecast. From 1955, however, there has been a marked increase especially in gonorrhoea in young women. Of the women who develop the disease 30 per cent are under 20.

Syphilis is first evident in the form of a painless ulcer which has certain typical features. It usually appears on the penis or on the lips of the vagina 10-20 days after exposure to the infection. The spirochaete can be cultured from the ulcer and the disease is also detectable by blood tests. Blood tests are crucial when complications of the original infection are suspected. The possible complications of syphilis in its later stages, if untreated, are so many and various that doctors are taught to think of it as a possibility in any puzzling case. Treatment with antibiotics has so greatly reduced their frequency that the doctor in general practice sees these complications relatively rarely nowadays.

Gonorrhoea presents itself in the male as pain on passing water together with a green yellow discharge from the penis. Diagnosis depends chiefly on bacteriological culture of the discharge. In women there may be a greenish vaginal discharge, but very frequently symptoms are absent or are so slight as to be unnoticed. Most female cases are diagnosed because their male partners are encouraged to bring them for tests.

This factor of absence of symptoms in infected women is one of the important reasons why the incidence of venereal disease remains high despite the fact that treatment with antibiotics is so effective. Untreated gonorrhoea may spread to the uterus and the Fallopian tubes where infection can result in permanent blockage of the tubes, thus causing infertility.

Non-specific urethritis resembles gonorrhoea in its symptoms except that the discharge is colourless. The causative agent is more difficult to detect: indeed there is an unresolved argument as to its nature and whether it is always the same. Although females may carry and transfer the disease, all the recognisable cases occur in men.

It will be seen from this brief account of the most common forms of venereal disease that it is of the greatest importance to detect these diseases early since their treatment is for the most part successful; when not treated they can result in far-reaching health complications (for example, in cases of secondary and tertiary syphilis). The identification and treatment of contacts of any person harbouring the infection is equally a very high priority. Because of the stigma attaching to venereal diseases, direct and anonymous access to special clinics is an important health service provision aimed at encouraging attendance. One important safeguard of anonymity and confidentiality in these clinics is that reports to patients' general practitioners are only sent with the patient's specific agreement. The majority of the special clinics have a social worker attached to them.

Illhealth in young women

The difference between the sexes in experience of disease and in the frequency of medical consultation in this age group is almost entirely accounted for by the impact of sexual life and childbirth and the stresses of caring for young children. Since childbirth is usually a normal physiological, and not a pathological, experience, increase in disease is not as great as the increased need for consultation, much of which is preventive (i.e. ante-natal and post-natal care).

Pregnancy and associated disorders

The care of the pregnant woman before and after delivery
has combined with improved economic and social conditions
to produce a dramatic fall in maternal deaths. The reduction in the number and severity of disorders before, during
and after delivery is more directly attributable to careful
medical surveillance. However, as the 'Report on Inequalities in Health' (18) clearly shows, there are considerable
social class and regional differences in both maternal mortality and morbidity, due to unequal provision of services in
different parts of the country and to the greater reluctance
of women in Social Classes IV and V to make use of them.
  95 per cent of babies in this country are now born in hospital – a change which has occurred in the last ten years.
Many women would prefer to have their second or third
babies at home, but at present the technical advantages and
safety of hospital care, even if confined to a couple of days
during and after the delivery, are felt by obstetricians to
outweigh the emotional advantages of childbirth in the
familiar surroundings of their own homes and attendance by
their general practitioner. To some extent the presence of
the husband at the birth (a relatively new practice and by no
means universal as yet) offsets the disadvantages of hospital
delivery.
  Hospital deliveries highlight the conflict which occurs in
other situations between 'purely' medical indications and the
broader considerations of health care. Many women find
their experience of giving birth in hospital both deperson-
alising and too 'medicalised' and therefore an impediment to
the satisfactory establishment of the mother/infant bond.
A good deal of criticism has recently been voiced by mothers
and the media about excessive resort to induction of births
and to analgesia during labour in many maternity departments. Some of these practices seem hard to justify on
grounds other than the convenience of staff and it is to be
hoped that they will be modified.
  If pregnancy, birth and the puerperium are usually
'normal', there is nevertheless the possibility of hazard and
pathology. Miscarriage is the first risk to arise – usually
between the fifth and twelfth week of pregnancy. The cause
is almost invariably obscure. Repeated miscarriage occurs
in a percentage of women and is a problem in the face of
which doctors are relatively helpless. In some cases such
measures as bedrest and careful attention to general health

in the early stages of pregnancy can prevent the loss of the foetus in vulnerable women.

A specific, though rare, danger in early pregnancy is an ectopic pregnancy, when the ovum becomes fertilised in one of the Fallopian tubes before reaching the cavity of the uterus. Such a pregnancy is not viable and it carries a serious risk of rupturing the tube in which it occurs. This causes bleeding into the abdominal cavity (peritoneum) which can endanger a woman's life: immediate surgical action is called for. Other important complications of pregnancy are a rise in blood pressure, urinary infection, and bleeding from the placenta (ante-partum haemorrhage).

Ante-natal care is designed to identify abnormal features and complications of pregnancy and also to detect such conditions as twin pregnancy and any unusual positions of the developing foetus which might cause difficulties at the time of delivery. The commonest of these is a breach presentation when the buttocks and the legs of the baby in utero are positioned to come first through the birth canal instead of the head.

The normal and abnormal methods of delivery are events with which social workers are unlikely to be involved in their professional capacity. What is important for them to realise, however, is that the safety of the mother and child depends on a close and regular supervision throughout the ante-natal period and sometimes too on a quick and decisive action at the time of birth. The latter may include the substitution of the normal vaginal delivery by a 'Caesarean' operation which entails opening up the abdominal cavity in order to lift out the baby.

A major dread of many parents expecting the birth of a child is the possibility of it being handicapped. As we have indicated earlier in this chapter, such a possibility is very real. In recent years it has become possible to detect certain congenital deformities so early in pregnancy that termination is a practical possibility for those who want it. Two of the conditions which can be thus detected are spina bifida and Down's syndrome. The techniques of scanning and amniocentesis are at present available to only a small proportion of pregnant women – those considered at special risk. When they become routine, however, they will create serious ethical dilemmas for many prospective parents. The choice between an abortion and knowingly giving birth to a handicapped child will be a hard and a painful one for many people. It will not be made easier by

the values and pressures of society, some of which will
favour policies based on what is eugenically desirable and
economically preferable.   Such attitudes could lead to a
situation where a decision, for instance,to have a mongol
child, might be condemned as socially irresponsible, carrying a stigma as grave as did unmarried motherhood in Victorian time.   One can well envisage a new set of personal
and social problems arising in which social workers might
be called upon to intervene alongside doctors and others.

The puerperium (post-delivery stage) may be complicated
by haemorrhage due to part of the placenta having been retained.   Other common problems are difficulty in establishing breast feeding or the development of a depressive
state.

The emphasis by doctors on breast feeding has varied
over the years and has been subject to certain fashions.
The preference for breast feeding has also been influenced
by prevailing cultural values and customs and the social
conditions under which mothers lived.   The present medical
position is that the advantages to the baby of breast feeding
over bottle feeding are generally stressed and mothers are
encouraged to breast feed.   Such advice is often counter-
acted, however, by the desire of many women to return to
work at the earliest possible opportunity and to be as independent of their babies as possible.

For most mothers, however welcome the baby, adjustment
to its constant needs imposes some degree of strain and
tiredness.   These normal reactions must be distinguished
from the pathological conditions such as a severe depression.   A degree of depression following delivery is not uncommon.   It is thought to be the result of a combination of
hormonal changes and the psychological reactions in adjusting to motherhood.   In the majority of instances the depression is short lived, especially when the baby was wanted
and there is a husband or a 'husband figure' to give the
mother the necessary support and reassurance.   Where, in
the absence of such assistance, or as a result of some personality deficiency in the mother, the depression persists
and results in a chronic state of apathy and withdrawal, the
newborn baby's health and development is at great risk.
The nature and the degree of social work intervention in
such circumstances will, of course, depend on the severity
of the mother's problem;   however, it usually entails both
some help in the actual care of the infant and practical and
psychological support to the mother and/or both parents.

A puerperal psychotic breakdown, though much less common, is very serious, potentially endangering the lives of both mother and infant; it has been known to lead to both infanticide and suicide. Treatment in a psychiatric in-patient unit is needed and some form of substitute care for the baby and any other children has to be arranged. Whilst some families can manage the situation without the help of a social worker, more often than not this is needed.

Diseases in young women unrelated to pregnancy

Urinary infections

These occur far more commonly in women than men and their incidence increases during the period of sexual activity.

If infection occurs in the bladder, passing water is pain-ful, particularly at the end of the act. Urination is more frequent both by night and by day. Infection spreading from the bladder up to the kidney causes pain in the loin and fever. Whereas an infected bladder may be merely incon-venient, an infected kidney is prostrating. The latter con-dition may be signalled by a rigor - a dramatic shivering and shaking associated with a sudden rise of body tempera-ture, which causes the patient to feel intensely cold and to call for blanket after blanket, only to throw them off as an excessive sense of heat ensues. Treatment is based on using an antibiotic which has been tested in the laboratory against the particular germs causing the illness. Such testing is important because the bacteria may change from attack to attack in the same person. Attacks can sometimes be prevented by maintaining a high intake of fluid and empty-ing the bladder before and after intercourse. Repeated attacks demand full investigation of the urinary tract to ensure that there is no underlying physiological cause which can be treated. While the bacteria responsible may be known and easily detected in the urine, the whole cause of this troublesome condition is not clear. That it occurs more often in women is obviously related to the anatomical fact that their bladder is separated from the exterior of the body by a distance of half an inch compared to about six inches in men, but it is often difficult to account for an attack on a particular occasion.

Vaginal discharges

It is normal for a woman to have a white vaginal discharge,
but seldom enough to appear on underclothes. A discharge
which stains the knickers may be abnormal and a yellow or
green discharge is always abnormal. There are a number
of causes of which some are serious. For this reason
medical investigation is always essential. As has already
been mentioned, several forms of venereal disease may be
the cause of vaginal discharge. A yellow discharge may
issue not from the vagina but from the uterus itself or from
the Fallopian tubes. The underlying infection usually
causes pain and fever and this makes it important for it to
be accurately diagnosed and speedily treated. There are
specific treatments which can be applied to each cause of
vaginal discharge.

Disorders of menstruation

Where menstrual loss is exceptionally heavy over a period
of time it can result in anaemia. Bleeding between periods
is also abnormal: both conditions require medical investigation.
   Premenstrual symptoms of anxiety, tension, irritability,
depression and certain physical symptoms like weight
increase and a sense of swelling are common in the week
before menstruation. They represent a change in the usual
balance of the hormones, but it is not known why some
women experience these changes so acutely while others
never do. The condition can be controlled by treatment.
Considering how commonly premenstrual tension occurs and
how much discomfort it causes, it is surprising that it was
recognised by doctors only relatively recently.

Disorders of the breast

Infection of the breast may occur during the period of
breast feeding. Before the era of antibiotics this used to
lead to the formation of an abscess, but with their help it
is now a condition easily controllable in most instances.
   At other times, the only important question, when anything seems amiss in the breast, is whether it is cancer.
Breast cancer normally shows itself as a single hard nodule

in one breast – usually noticed by the woman herself, but not necessarily very quickly. It is almost invariably pain-less. It can occur in young women but the incidence rises later. It cannot be proved or disproved without at least a small surgical operation. It is, of course, also important to know whether the cancer has already spread to other sites in the body. Spread is much more probable if there is an enlargement of the lymph gland in the armpit, which are directly related to the breast but, even when these appear normal, it is impossible to be sure that dispersion of cancer cells through the blood stream has not already begun.

Treatment of a malignant growth usually involves removal of part or all of the breast, followed by a course of radio-therapy to decrease the risk of spread. In addition to the trauma inherent in the mutilating nature of the treatment itself, the uncertainty about its effectiveness is a source of considerable stress to most people. Only time can tell whether or not any cancerous cells have remained in the body to cause further trouble.

To most women the loss of a breast constitutes a serious threat to their body image and often leads to strong emotion-al reactions. The effects of this mutilation on the marital relationship can also be considerable. The serious nature of these complications indicates the advisability of social work help being readily available to these women and their husbands.

Benign tumours, some of them cystic, do occur in the breast. They are called benign because they do not spread to other parts or cause general illness or death.

It is not infrequent for women to complain of pain in the breasts, often combined with multiple soft nodules which appear and disappear. The misleading word 'mastitis' is applied to describe the condition, suggesting an infection, when in fact the symptoms are due to an ill-understood endocrine influence. There is no worthwhile treatment, but careful examination and reassurance about the nature of the condition are essential.

Illness in young men

This relatively healthy age group is prone, though much less frequently, to most of the disorders which afflict older men and which will be discussed in subsequent sections of

this chapter.   The only disorders which occur more frequently in the younger group are injuries.   Young people
are often more exposed to physical danger and damage and
prone to take more risks than their elders.

Injuries may occur to almost any part of the body, but
some parts are affected with greater frequency: the hands,
legs, back and head are particularly vulnerable.   It is
essentially the skin and musculo-skeletal system that sustain damage.   The skin is vulnerable to cuts and lacera-
tions, to grazing and bruising; the musculo-skeletal
system (muscles, joints and bones) to sprains (tears) of the
ligaments related to joints, of muscles where they are
attached to bones, or of their tendons, and to fractures in
the bones.   Back injuries and head injuries are more
complex.

The back is liable to injury when a person is carrying
heavy weights.   This is particularly true when the back is
bent forward, as in lifting something from the ground,
because the structure of the back is then at a mechanical
disadvantage.   The spinal column consists essentially of
25 small bones (vertebrae) held together partly by ligaments
and partly by the intervertebral discs formed of cartilage,
which act as shock absorbers - they are less hard and more
mobile than the word cartilage might imply.   When the back
is bent forward and there is a sudden stress from above
downwards on the whole vertebral column, the cartilaginous
discs receive the stress, but tend to be forced backwards.
As their centres are soft like a firm jelly, their integrity
depends on the strength of their exterior hard coat, particularly at the back.   If this stretches or breaks by a
sudden pressure, the disc comes into immediate contact
either with the spinal cord (the central nerve of the whole
body) which lies immediately behind them, or with the peripheral nerves which spring from the spinal cord on each
side at the level of each disc.   Pressure on these nerves
in a confined space causes pain, but pain will not necessarily be felt at the back itself, it may be experienced at
the other extremity of the nerve, for instance, in the hand
or the foot.   This is the meaning of 'referred pain', an
important phenomenon in medicine.   Thus pain may be
caused at or close to the point where it is felt; alternatively its cause may lie at a distance.   'Sciatic pain' or
'sciatica' may be felt only in the foot, but its cause is
likely to be near the small of the back.

In young people, where unlike older people the back has

not suffered prolonged stresses, it is usually a major sudden physical effort which causes trouble.

Methods of investigating disorders of the back are inadequate at present so that it is often difficult to make a precise diagnosis. Methods of treatment are also relatively unsatisfactory. Fortunately most back pains respond to a natural process of recovery, usually within five days. The one method of treatment which can be relied on, especially in the early stages, is rest on a flat surface in the horizontal position, presumably because this removes most of the pressure on the affected joint from the weight of the upper part of the body. It is in relation to back problems that osteopathy or manipulation has its chief application and is another frequently effective method of treatment.

Head injuries affect the scalp, the skull, the brain, or the blood vessels of the brain. Of these the injuries to the scalp and the skull are the least important, although the most obvious. In itself, a fracture of the skull is not serious; it matters in so far as the brain is also affected.

Concussion means a shock to the brain. Any blow to the head moves the brain within the skull. The brain is to some extent protected because it lies in a thin covering of fluid and contains more of the same fluid at its own centre. Anything more than a minor blow is likely to result in a shock which causes transient loss of consciousness, with subsequent headache and loss of memory for the moment of impact and the events just before this. Complete recovery usually results within days, but the longer the loss of consciousness the slower the recovery.

Much more rarely, a blow to the head results in gradual loss of consciousness after an interval of days, weeks or months. There is also a slow increase of headache as consciousness dims. In these circumstances it is likely that the injury has caused a leak of blood on the surface of the brain resulting in pressure on this vital organ in its confined space (subdural haematoma). This is an important but relatively rare injury.

Fractures of the skull may be accompanied by laceration of the brain substance near the fracture or by injury to a blood vessel on the surface of the brain, with results similar to those of subdural haematoma, but more immediate and rapid. There will be deep and prolonged unconsciousness, with signs of paralysis in limbs. Urgent surgical intervention is then necessary.

The commonest fracture is that above the wrist, involving

the radius and ulna bones of the forearm (Colles' fracture).
The next commonest is fracture above the ankle, involving
the tibia and fibula (Pott's fracture). In both instances two
bones are broken. But if there is a single break in each,
the problem of treatment is relatively straightforward – to
see that the bones are realigned end to end and then held in
the correct position by a plaster splint until reunion has
taken place by a natural process which usually requires a
few weeks. Where several fragments of a bone result from
a fracture, the problem of realignment is more complicated,
but essentially the same. Difficulties increase if a broken
end of a bone is forced through the skin, since this intro-
duces the possibility of secondary infection occurring.
Before antiobiotics were available, infection of bone was a
very serious problem, difficult to treat; it still requires
very rigorous treatment even with the present resources at
medical disposal.

Some of the most distressing conditions in young people
are those resulting from road accidents. These can often
transform a strong and healthy individual into a physical
wreck. Injuries of the spinal cord, depending on where
they have occurred, lead to varying degrees of paralysis:
paraplegia, tetraplegia or quadriplegia. Paralysis of the
lower limbs is often accompanied by incontinence.

Many of the road accidents are preventable, especially
when they result from drunkenness or reckless driving.
The rising incidence of drink abuse among young people and
the increasing popularity of the motor cycle make it likely
that the problem will escalate unless energetic preventive
measures are taken to combat what is both a serious social
problem and one which involves much individual suffering.

MIDDLE-AGED PERSONS (AGE GROUP 36-64)

Such a large age group can be regarded as an entity only
with difficulty. Whereas for the 36-year-olds the future
may still stretch a long way forward and possibilities of
change and satisfying ambition for self and family are wide
open, for those in their 60s the situation is very different.
They will have already experienced some diminishing of
their powers and they have to acknowledge that their remaining life span may not be that long.

The background to disease in middle age

Certain inevitable developmental changes happen to people in this age group. The menopause in women is the most obvious example. It forms a vulnerable period of life and at this time many women are more sensitive to hurtful experiences and more liable to certain forms of ill health, in addition to the inevitable physical changes of the climacteric.

The biological aspects of the menopause are inextricably linked to the social and psychological factors operative in middle age. These include the difficulties of dealing with adolescent children as they struggle painfully to gain their independence, the departure of the family from home and the discovery by the couple that they are alone together again, and the 'mid-life crisis' – the realisation that life does not stretch forward indefinitely. 'Have I achieved anything?' 'Shall I achieve anything?'; 'Is there still time to do better or to do something different?' – these are the kinds of questions asked by most people at some stage during this age period. For those who are single the possibilities of marriage, children and a family life are waning with increasing rapidity.

Many people in this age group, both married and single, carry in addition to their other life tasks responsibilities for the care of ageing parents or other relations. This can be a heavy burden both in practical terms and psychologically.

Given the young age at which many women now complete their family, a woman of 36 may experience both the satisfaction of maternal achievement and the relief of fewer demands on her domestic role, thus feeling free to pursue her own interests. These may entail either resuming her former employment or looking for new opportunities. If she lacks such outlets, she may feel a loss of purpose in her life. Her predicament may be particularly acute if her need for adaptation to her new circumstances coincides with the onset of the menopause. This may aggravate her regrets about lost youth and exacerbate feelings of jealousy of her children who are entering into adolescence or young adulthood with all its attractions no longer available to her.

At 36 most men are at the height of pursuit of their career and this time can be particularly stressful to those who fail to satisfy their ambitions or who feel that they are losing out in the competitive struggle for promotion and

advancement generally (not to mention those who are
unemployed).

Both men and women have to face the fact that somewhere
about the age of 40 life is half over. The gradual physical
deterioration of their bodies reminds them of this and gives
rise to the psychological need to face up to the thought of
death.

The particular challenge of the middle-age period lies in
the way it tests the adequacy of the individual's sense of
personal identity - the extent to which he or she knows what
they stand for, what their life objectives and achievements
have been and are being envisaged for the future, and
whether or not they have been able to come to terms with
failings and disappointments. Such a challenge can at best
be met only to a relative degree, even by the most mature
people, so it is not surprising that for many middle age is a
difficult and even a critical period. Strained marital relations, a sense of loneliness and sadness are common manifestations, as well as various bodily symptoms. We discuss
more fully the problems of loneliness, and the part which
social workers can play in its relief, in Chapter 5. What
needs emphasising here is the need for social workers, as
well as doctors, to be on the lookout for the manifestations
of the 'mid-life crisis' in those individuals who seek their
help with a variety of symptoms and problems.

Whilst, as we have already suggested, some degree of
the 'mid-life crisis' is commonly experienced, the impact of
a serious disease accompanying it can be all the more dis-
astrous. Among such diseases, not infrequent in this age
group, are those of arteries (as in the case of Mr Harrison
in Chapter 3, for example) and cancer in its many forms.
These can totally incapacitate or destroy men and women in
their full vigour who should have had many valuable contributions still to make.

The menopause

The mean age for the menopause is 49, but it may occur as
early as 35 and as late as 55. It results from changes in
the behaviour of endocrine glands, the ovaries and the
pituitary gland particularly. These cause the cessation of
menstruation and put an end to the capacity to bear children.
(There is however no necessary accompanying change in
sexual desire or performance.) A proportion of women

find the manifestations of the menopause physically and
psychologically disturbing. The period of such disturbance may last only for a few weeks or months, but in some
women it may extend for several years. A common symptom
is the occurrence of hot flushes, but there are also many
others like those which are associated with premenstrual
tension, discussed earlier in the chapter. In both situations many women still fail to receive appropriate help from
their doctors, who either ignore their symptoms or do not
take them sufficiently seriously.

As far as men are concerned, there is a lack of agreement
within the medical profession as to the extent to which
changes in the sexual functioning of men aged 50 and over
are equivalent to the menopause in women. Although the
male climacteric does not produce equally tangible manifestations and male fertility continues for very much longer,
there is nevertheless a growing body of opinion that there
are detectable changes, both physical and psychological,
which can be linked to sexual change.

Gynaecological problems in middle-aged women

Variations in menstrual bleeding

Although for many women the menopause involves a gradual
diminution in the frequency and the intensity of menstrual
bleeding, for some it is heralded by increased frequency or
heavier bleeding. Alternatively, the normal monthly cycle
may be disturbed and irregular bleeding replace it.

Heavy or irregular menstrual bleeding can simply be an
indication of the menopause starting, but it can also be a
sign of disease. The greatest hazard is that of cancer
located at the neck of the uterus, within its cavity, or in
an ovary. If there are clear intervals without bleeding or
discharge of any sort, anxiety is less justified, but physical
examination of the vagina, uterus and ovaries is nevertheless an important safeguard. Such an examination can be
carried out by a general practitioner. A cervical smear
may be advisable in addition. This entails a simple scraping of the neck of the uterus to obtain material which is then
tested in a laboratory for early evidence of cancer at this
site (such a test cannot either indicate or deny the presence
of cancer within the cavity of the uterus, in an ovary, or
anywhere else in the body). Where there is real doubt

about the cause of irregular or heavy bleeding, it is essential that the cavity of the uterus itself be examined. This can be done by a gynaecologist only, by dilating the opening of the uterus and scraping its internal lining (a 'D&C' operation).

If either of these tests indicate cancer, treatment either by surgery or radiotherapy, or both, is essential. Although limited surgical removal is sometimes sufficient, the commonest intervention is total removal of the uterus (hysterectomy). Depending on the seriousness of the problem, one or both ovaries may also be removed.

Hysterectomy

Cancer is not the only reason for removing the uterus. A significant degree of anaemia caused by heavy menstruation can result in the woman feeling continuously unwell, and removal of the womb becomes the only means of correcting the situation. Benign tumours - fibroids - in the walls of the uterus, besides being the cause of excessive bleeding, may become so large that they interfere with such normal physiological functions as micturition and defaecation. It may not be possible to remove them simply and this means that hysterectomy is the only choice.

The removal of the uterus in a woman before the menopause obviously puts an end to any chance of conceiving children, but it does not usually influence sexual desire or performance. Nor does it induce other changes associated with the menopause, unless the ovaries are also removed.

The emotional reactions of women to the operation vary greatly. At one extreme, some feel nothing but relief, whether from inconvenience of the previous symptoms, anxiety about serious disease, or worry about continuing risks of childbirth. At the other extreme, like a mastectomy, a hysterectomy can be experienced as a mutilation and an assault on femininity.

Disease prevalence in middle age

During the 30 years covered by this age span there is a general rise in the liability to death and illness as indicated by consultations in general practice, certification of absence from work, figures for hospital admissions, and the Registrar-General's statistics on registered deaths.

Comparing the two sexes, there is a more marked increase in consultation rates for women than for men, but not in actual absence from work due to sickness. This indicates a greater readiness on the part of women to seek medical advice.

The important causes of death before the age of 65 are, in order of frequency: ischaemic heart disease (heart attacks), malignant new growths of all types, 'strokes' (cerebral thrombosis and haemorrhage), bronchitis and pneumonia. In theory, a considerable proportion of deaths from all these conditions are preventable, but it would be wrong to claim that this is equally true in practice. For example, carcinoma of the lung accounts for nearly half of all deaths before the age of 65 which are due to malignant growths. The incidence of carcinoma of the lung in doctors is much lower than in the general population due to a difference in smoking habits. Doctors are the only group in the population who have sharply reduced the habit of smoking cigarettes as a result of the evidence that smoking and lung cancer are closely linked. It is because of the discrepancy between what is known and the willingness to act upon the knowledge that deaths due to carcinoma of the lung and bronchus, coronary thrombosis, and bronchitis are only preventable <u>in theory</u> at present.

We shall discuss many of the other diseases prevalent in middle age in the later chapters of the book, especially in Chapters 5 and 6, as they are not exclusive to this age group, but also because their general importance favours their discussion in a broader context.

The issues of screening and of 'routine checks'

It is the custom, particularly in the United States of America, but also for certain privileged groups in the population here, to attend regularly for a comprehensive 'health check'. Essentially, these checks are an attempt to detect a disease early. However, there are only a few disorders capable of early detection which are both common and symptomless and can be successfully controlled by treatment. For this reason routine checks are warranted only in relation to a few conditions. The most obvious examples of these are raised blood pressure and diabetes mellitus.

Some people attempt to justify routine checks for all on

the additional grounds that they can identify rare disorders which can be treated. This assumes, however, that such disorders would not be noticed by those who suffer from them, that medical help would not be sought and that they would be missed by the patient's doctor. Regarding conditions for which there is no effective treatment, attempts to identify these by means of routine screening raise doubts of ethical, economic and psychological nature. Apart from the financial costs involved, on humane grounds it is often better that the person concerned does not have to live with the knowledge of having an incurable disease before its symptoms make it an inescapable reality. In general, the problem of the increased anxiety and disease consciousness which is a frequent by-product of 'routine health checks', should not be ignored. Whatever their relative advantages and disadvantages, such checks have, so far, not been officially favoured in Britain.

The alternative approach in general use is to select groups in the population which are shown by the statistics of morbidity to be particularly vulnerable and then to monitor their health regularly. Old people and young children are an obvious case in point. The importance of regular health supervision in the case of children is further enhanced by the fact that this offers opportunities to influence morbid processes at the earliest possible stage of their manifestation.

Pregnant women form another 'vulnerable group' on which a concentration of attention produces demonstrable advantages. As we have already shown, an early detection of ill health in the expectant mother, of abnormalities of the foetus, its position in the uterus as well as abnormalities in the uterus itself and the placenta, can lead to action at a stage when this is highly effective.

With regard to middle-aged persons, routine checks covering all possibilities of disease as in the case of children, do not seem at present to be justifiable. Since this is an age group in which most members attend their doctors at least once a year (70 per cent do so), the simplest approach to ensure that the three aspects of health which are of particular significance in preventive terms - blood pressure, sugar content in the urine and body weight - are regularly monitored is for these to be checked during the patient's consultation with his general practitioner, whatever may be the reason for this.

General health needs in middle age

Medical evidence accumulates about certain general needs for maintaining health in middle age. It confirms to a large extent many traditional beliefs.

The work of Morris and others (19) has demonstrated the need to maintain habits of exercise throughout life. And yet, physical exercise often diminishes at this time with a decline in the practice of sport and a tendency to increasingly sedentary occupation.

Smoking has been increasingly shown to undermine health. So far, attempts to help people to stop smoking have been largely ineffective, but it must be hoped that the efforts by the Health Education Council and other bodies to discourage young people from starting to smoke will ultimately result in more success.

Both excessive eating and consumption of alcohol are important factors in undermining health. The Royal College of Psychiatrists has recently published its views on the quantities of beer, spirits and wine consumption above which the health danger begins. (20) That report is only one manifestation of the growing alarm at the prevalence of drink abuse in this country.

An excessive preoccupation with work constitutes a danger for a relatively small proportion of the population. For them periods of relaxation and change of activity are important in terms of both immediate effects and long-term gains. There is a very real danger in store when they retire for those for whom work excludes all other interests. Preparation for retirement is therefore an important preventive factor in relation to health in middle age. Its value is twofold: it can contribute to a much happier and more fulfilled old age, and it can also enrich current life by bringing into it a wider perspective and by making it less exclusively tied to current problems and responsibilities.

OLD PEOPLE (AGE GROUP 65 AND ABOVE)

The proportion of old people in the population is large – there are at present over 7.5 million of those who have reached and passed retirement age. Of these, just under 3 million are over 75 years of age and this 'old old' group will be increasing in both absolute numbers and in relation to the rest of the population during the next few decades.

These figures mean that both doctors and social workers will increasingly need to devote their professional time and effort to work with the elderly.

In considering the health characteristics and the needs of old people it is helpful to differentiate between the younger members of this group – the young old – and those who are very old, i.e. those over 75 years. There are many misconceptions about health in old age. Some of these stem from failure to distinguish between 'senescence' which is a term for the normal biological process of ageing, and 'senility' which denotes pathological changes in the brain affecting behaviour.

The relationship between chronological age, organic brain change and abnormality of behaviour is far from being straightforward. Some very old people remain mentally alert and active whilst some younger ones exhibit signs of severe senility. Post-mortem examinations of brain tissue do not reveal a direct relationship between the extent of organic change and the degree of behavioural abnormality.

An important general feature of health in old age is that whilst the incidence of illness in old people does not appear to be much greater than in middle-aged persons, the duration of an illness is usually longer and the recovery from it is considerably slower. This has important implications for the medical care of old people; it is important to intervene at an early stage of an illness and there is a particular need for proper rehabilitation following it.

Owing to the relatively low status of old people in our society, in which they themselves often acquiesce, there is an excessively low expectation about their entitlement to health and general well-being. This is both true for themselves and for the various 'service providers' (including doctors and social workers). There is a widespread tendency to view old age and ill health as synonymous; this results in undue pessimism about the effectiveness of intervention in the health problems of the elderly. Another reason why old people are often reluctant to seek medical help is that admission of ill health carries a particular threat to them – it is a foretaste of physical and/or social death as Johnson has argued. (21)

For these various reasons many old people are deprived of relief from such relatively easily treatable symptoms as those of mild anaemia, sore feet, constipation, difficulty in chewing food due to ill-fitting dentures, poor vision and hearing. The situation becomes further exacerbated when

resources are scarce and difficult decisions have to be made
about priorities.   Failure to give proper attention to the
health needs of old people reflects a sad lack of regard for
the potential quality of life in old age.

Quality of life implies social and psychological as well as
physical well-being.   Old people are particularly vulnerable in all these areas.   Factors of general importance
such as physical comfort, warmth and an adequate diet
assume special significance in old age on account of the
reduced mobility, low body temperature, and weakened
digestion which accompany senescence.

Owing to the ever-rising cost of heating, coupled with the
poor structural quality of many of the houses in which old
people live, the problem of hypothermia (abnormally low
body temperature) in old people has assumed very large
proportions.   According to Age Concern, no less than
45,000 old people a year die from the condition, although
only a very small number are listed under that category in
the official death statistics.   The serious nature and the
prevalence of hypothermia has been established by
Wicks, (22) following a painstaking study of the problem.

In the psychological sphere, loneliness and a sense of
worthlessness are common.   The increasing need for
dependence with advancing years and failing strength is
frequently accompanied by the need to assert the last ves-
tiges of independence for fear of losing personal autonomy.
This results in particular sensitivity on the part of old
people to intervention in their lives by others which can
sometimes take the form of abrasiveness or suspicion.

The extent of old people's social and psychological needs,
coupled with their greater physical vulnerability, points to
the importance of the contribution social workers can make
to the enhancement of the quality of life during this period
in terms of both social well-being and health.   In social
work with old people the importance of the 'hows' as well
as of the 'whats' is particularly pertinent, although, sadly,
it tends to be more frequently overlooked than in contacts
with people in the other age groups.   Because of the problems regarding dependence which have already been mentioned, old people have an even greater need than many
other clients to feel secure in a relationship of mutual trust
and respect before they can feel free to accept help without
feeling denigrated or personally diminished by it.   This
fact has important practical implications for the conduct of
social workers.   One of these is the need for care in 'going

at the client's pace'. Such a pace in the case of old
people is often a very slow one and this calls in turn for
considerable patience and time. Most old people are psychologically as well as physically incapable of hurry and
any attempts to rush them beyond their capacity are bound
to result in distress and confusion. As in work with any
other group of clients, the success of social work with old
people depends on the following three major conditions being
met: a genuine liking and respect for them; an appropriate
knowledge and understanding of their needs; and specific
skills in applying these attitudes and this knowledge in
practice.

One of the problems which many doctors and social
workers experience in working with old people stems from
their own unresolved feelings about old age. This is often
viewed in almost exclusively negative terms, as a 'gateway
to death', rather than as a period in life, which, like any
other period, has both its own special gratifications and
frustrations and presents its own unique maturational challenge. One of the best-known exponents of the latter view,
Ericson, presents the distinct developmental characteristics of old age in terms of the dichotomy between 'ego
integrity' and 'ego despair'. (23) The maturational task of
old age is thus to achieve the former and overcome the
latter. Success in carrying out this task results in a truly
integrated personality, a remarkable achievement possible
only in old age.

Such a positive view of old age provides a sound raison
d'être for work with old persons aimed at assisting them to
reach the important objective of 'ego integrity' (and thus
health too). That the attainment of this objective is far
from easy cannot be disputed. This is particularly true in
our society, which, by putting a premium on tangible
material achievements, denigrates such 'inner' values as
those of reflection, self-knowledge, self-respect, wisdom,
generosity, and serenity. No one, however, who has had
the privilege of knowing an old person endowed with these
qualities can doubt their worth, or the value of striving
after them.

One way in which social workers can assist old people is
by recognising the value of reminiscence and by acting upon
such recognition. Reminiscence is a feature of old age
which is often badly misunderstood. Not infrequently it is
viewed in an entirely negative light instead of being recognised for what it is, namely a positive manifestation of an

old person's ability to cope. Pincus (24) lists four main
functions of reminiscence in old age: to maintain a sense of
personal identity and self-respect; to provide the means by
which a review of past life becomes possible; to help
resolve grief; to deal with specific stressful experience.
Viewed in such a light, far from being a manifestation of
senility, reminiscence is a sign of health and of adaptability.   It is its absence and not its presence that should be
cause for concern.   Social workers can facilitate constructive reminiscence by encouraging it in their contacts with
old people, by confirming its value through interested and
intelligent listening, and by responding appropriately.
Such assistance may call for skilled social work or it may
be undertaken by others according to individual circumstances.   But it must be a cause for concern that its value is
not sufficiently recognised because this is to the detriment
of many old persons.   For example, the study by Steven-
son, Parsloe et al. (25) has clearly demonstrated the extent
of negative discrimination in many local authority social
services departments where old people's needs are frequently assumed to require only straightforward welfare
services such as home helps, meals or chiropody, and work
with them is therefore automatically allocated to welfare
assistants.
   The health and the well-being of people is not only
dependent on their receiving appropriate help from others,
but also on the availability to them of opportunities to be of
some use to their fellow men.   Old people are no exception
to this.   Social workers must therefore be sensitive to the
needs of elderly people in this respect.   The needs of
individuals to contribute to the good of the community are
balanced by the community's needs.   The large number of
'young old' people within the community constitutes a rich
potential for various forms of helping activity, such as
babysitting, visiting the sick and lonely, both in their homes
and in hospitals, acting as readers to the blind, etc.   A
more active involvement of old people in community life than
is often the case at present makes good sense in relation to
all the aspects of community health and well-being: individual, social and economic.

Disease in old age

There are three diseases occurring during this age period
which are normally not to be found among the middle aged.
Not surprisingly they all belong to the group termed
'degenerative diseases' – an important category from the
pathological point of view. Of these, clinically the most
important is dementia ('loss of mind'), a state which shows
itself in forgetfulness for recent events, repetition of
questions and stories, increasing difficulty in understanding anything that is new, and a general narrowing of
interest. These manifestations betray an ageing process
in the brain which is irreversible, but can be influenced to
a limited extent by temporary stimulation through company
and occupation. Dementia appears to be hastened by bore-
dom and loneliness. Sometimes what are mistakenly
thought to be symptoms of a progressive dementia may in
fact be those of a depressive state. Such states are also
common in old age and they can often be relieved or cut
short by treatment; the features are distinguishable from
dementia if careful account is taken.
  Another degenerative disease belonging particularly to
this age group is Parkinsonism. This affects mobility:
the limbs stiffen; walking is slowed and characterised by
small paces; the face loses expression, and there is a
noticeable tremor of the hand, the thumb and forefinger
especially. This condition is less common than dementia,
but important in its effects and its downhill course. It is,
however, treatable and treatment both relieves symptoms
and postpones the inevitable deterioration.
  A common feature of advanced old age is an increased
liability to falls, whether through failure of attention or
unsteadiness of gait, or those sudden and ill-understood
events called 'drop-attacks'. Falls are much more likely
to result in serious damage at this age because, owing to
the presence of senile osteoporosis – the third degenerative disease of old age – bones are now more brittle.
Fractures are therefore common, especially those of the
hip.
  Apart from these three major degenerative conditions and
a few others, less common, diseases in this age group do
not differ in their distribution from those affecting the
middle aged. There are, however, important differences
in the presentation of the different diseases and their
course. In general, symptoms are less pronounced. For

example, heart attacks – normally accomapnied by severe chest pain – can occur without pain; a malignant growth can develop in the stomach or the colon without causing symptoms until the pathological process is far advanced. The progress of diseases also differs, in general being slower; a malignant growth in the breast may run so slow and harmless a course that treatment is unnecessary and death is likely to be due to some other unrelated happening. An important general characteristic of any disease at this age is that it tends to leave the old person one stage older and less fit than he or she was before the illness; a complete return to the state of health prior to the disease is also unlikely. This may apply even to something as relatively simple as influenza. At best full recovery may take many months.

It is often difficult to distinguish disease in old people from the slower processes of degeneration which affect particularly the eyes, leading to such conditions as cataract, glaucoma or retinal degeneration; the ears – senile deafness; the joints – osteoarthritis; and the arteries – arteriosclerosis which limits the blood supply to organs served by an artery, whether it be the heart muscle, some part of the brain or the muscles of the leg.

Another typical characteristic of ill health in this age group is that problems are almost never single. If an old person comes to a doctor, it will usually be with more than one physical complaint. It is partly for this reason that old people often require the concurrent use of several medicines. This can in turn lead to difficulties if they are forgetful, or relatively incompetent to deal with more complex situations. This is just one aspect of a more general problem facing a proportion of old people who live alone and whose decreasing ability to manage is a cause of considerable concern to doctors, nurses and social workers alike. There are more women than men in this group because of women's greater longevity.

As we have already said, old people tend to consult doctors too little, as they will put up with difficulties for which help is available. Minor foot problems such as corns and painful toenails are neglected particularly often; the extent to which they have been limiting mobility and causing discomfort is often revealed only after these defects have been put right. These and similar problems indicate the value of geriatric health visitors who by visiting old people at home regularly can keep an eye on their health more effectively than can usually be achieved by general practitioners alone.

A minority of old people reach very advanced years with mind and body relatively unimpaired. They provide a challenge to all in society, although the causes of such successful longevity are by no means well understood. The following case illustration is concerned with an instance of such positive ageing.

Mrs Black was 89 years old when the social worker met her in the outpatients' department of a London hospital. She had been residing for the past few years in a small home for old people in one of the home counties. Following her husband's death some 15 years before, she had lived on her own, but then entered the home when she began finding this difficult to manage. She had several children and many other relations with whom she maintained close contact, but preferred to be independent of them. She had come to visit a great niece in London a few days before and, whilst with her, had developed an acute abdominal pain. The great niece brought her to the hospital on her general practitioner's advice. Whilst waiting to see the specialist, Mrs Black collapsed in the outpatient clinic with cerebral thrombosis. She lost consciousness and was admitted to hospital. The attack came as a great shock to the great niece who said that, except for high blood pressure, her great aunt had been in very good health.

Mrs Black made a speedy and a satisfactory recovery from this upset. She was somewhat confused during the first few days, but this was partly due to the disorientation caused by the strange surroundings in which she found herself. Once she regained her mental equilibrium, she proved to be as described by her great niece, an intelligent, alert and serene old lady whose age had clearly not been preventing her from enjoying life.

Mrs Black's good recovery from her 'stroke' was, however, accompanied by a persistence of her abdominal pain. This was found on investigation to be due to fairly severe diverticulitis. As the condition was not responding to medical treatment, reluctantly the doctors suggested surgery. However, to their relief (one suspects) Mrs Black adamantly refused to be operated on. She told the social worker that she had known two people with 'holes in their sides' and that she would not have one herself for anything in the world. However, her fear of a colostomy was only one reason for her refusal. An important factor lay in her general philosophy of life - she felt that at her age it was right to prepare for death rather than to think of prolonging life. Death did not constitute a dread for her – she regarded it not only as something natural and inevitable, but she also welcomed it as she felt she had lived long enough. This attitude towards death was accompanied by a mature readiness to wait for it and to make the most of life meanwhile. Thus she was very anxious indeed to return as soon as possible to the home which was her home and she became quite impatient when various inevitable delays over her discharge occurred. Some of her impatience was related to her being very anxious to spend her 90th birthday back in the home, surrounded by her family and friends.

When the day of her discharge came the farewells of the hospital staff who knew her reflected the profound affection and respect which everyone had developed for her in the course of her few weeks' stay on the ward.

After another few weeks the social worker received a warm letter from Mrs Black thanking her for her concern and help and enclosing a photograph from her 90th birthday celebration. The letter included the following sentence: 'I have had a very happy day and it was so particularly nice to spend one's last birthday in such a way'.

A few weeks later she was notified by Mrs Black's relatives that the old lady had died of another attack of cerebral thrombosis.

SUGGESTIONS FOR FURTHER READING

Given the range of material we have attempted to handle in this chapter, additional reading in many of the areas touched upon is of particular importance if their significance is to be fully appreciated.

We have divided our suggestions into three main sections: normal development; problems in development (including social disadvantages, physical and mental disabilities in children, and medical problems in relation to all age groups); social work in relation to particular client groups and health problems.

Normal development

N.J. Sheridan (1975), 'A Developmental Progress of Infants and Young Children', HMSO.
J. Bowlby (1969), 'Attachment and Loss', vol. I 'Attachment', Hogarth Press.

M. Rutter (1972), 'Maternal Deprivation Reassessed',
Penguin.
E.H. Ericson (1962), 'Identity, Youth and Crisis', Faber.
M. Schofield (1965), 'The Sexual Life of Young People',
Penguin.
M. Rutter, J. Tizard and K. Whitmore (1970), 'Education,
Health and Behaviour', Longman.
E. Rayner (1978), 'Human Development', Allen & Unwin.
A. Storr (1969), 'The Integrity of the Personality',
Penguin.
A. Maslow (1973), 'The Further Reaches of Human Nature',
Penguin.
J. and E. Newson (1968), 'Four Years Old in an Urban
Community', Penguin.
J. and E. Newson (1975), 'Seven Years Old in the Home
Environment', Allen & Unwin.
G. Gorer (1971), 'Sex and Marriage in England To-day',
Nelson.
M. Schofield (1973), 'The Sexual Behaviour of Young
Adults', Allen Lane.
E.J. Anthony and T. Benedec (eds) (1970), 'Parenthood:
Its Psychology and Psychopathology', Little Brown.
R. Skynner (1976), 'One Flesh, Separate Persons',
Constable.
L. Pincus (1960), 'Marriage: Studies in Emotional Conflict
and Growth', Methuen.
B.L. Neugarten (1967), 'Personality in Middle Age and
Late Life', Atherton.
J.H. Wallis (1962), 'The Challenge of Middle Age', Rout-
ledge & Kegan Paul.
D.B. Bromley (1969), 'The Psychology of Human Ageing',
Penguin.
D. Hobman (ed.) (1978), 'The Social Challenge of Ageing',
Croom Helm.
V. Carter and P. Liddiard (eds) (1978), 'An Ageing Popula-
tion: A Reader and Source Book', Open University.

Problems in development

J. McDaniel (1961), 'Physical Disability and Human Behav-
iour', Pergammon.
L. Burton (1975), 'The Family Life of Sick Children',
Routledge & Kegan Paul.
L. Lambert and J. Streather (1980), 'Children in Changing

Families', Macmillan for the National Children's Bureau.
M. Rutter (1975), 'Helping Troubled Children', Penguin.
R. Holman (1970), 'Trading in Children: A Study of Private
Fostering', Routledge & Kegan Paul.
'Report of the Committee on One Parent Families' (1974),
HMSO.
A.W. Franklin (ed.) (1975), 'Concerning Child Abuse',
Churchill Livingstone.
E. Younghusband, D. Birchall, R. Davies and M.L. Kelmer
Pringle (1970), 'Living with Handicap', National Bureau for
Cooperation in Child Care.
R. Lansdown (1980, 'More than Sympathy - The Everyday
Needs of Sick and Handicapped Children and their Families',
Tavistock.
D. Marsden (1969), 'Mothers Alone: Poverty and the Father-
less Family', Penguin.
V. George and P. Wilding (1972), 'Motherless Families',
Routledge & Kegan Paul.
D. Thomas (1978), 'The Social Psychology of Childhood
Disability', Methuen.
E. Anderson and B. Spain (1977), 'The Child with Spina
Bifida', Methuen.
M. Stacey et al. (1970), 'Hospitals, Children and their
Families', Routledge & Kegan Paul.
S. Gregory (1976), 'The Deaf Child and his Family', Allen
& Unwin.
B. Fried (1967), 'The Middle Age Crisis', Harper & Row.
A.H. Crisp (1980), 'Anorexia Nervosa: Let me be',
Academic Press.
S. McLeod (1981), 'The Art of Starvation: An Adolescence
Observed', Virago.
H. Gavron (1966), 'Captive Wives', Penguin.
J. Dominian (1976), 'Marital Breakdown', Penguin.
H. Dicks (1967), 'Marital Tensions', Routledge & Kegan
Paul.
B. Pitt (1974), 'Psychogeriatrics', Churchill Livingstone.
M. Wicks (1978), 'Old and Cold: Hypothermia and Social
Policy', Heinemann.
Report of a Special Committee of the Royal College of Psy-
chiatrists (1979), 'Alcohol and Alcoholism', Tavistock.
J. Orford and J. Harwin (1981), 'Alcohol and the Family',
Croom Helm.

Social work

Central Council for the Education and Training in Social
Work (1978), 'Good Enough Parenting: Report of a Group on
Work with Children'.
British Association of Social Workers (1975), 'Social Work
in Child Care'.
J. Mattinson and I. Sinclair (1979), 'Mate and Stalemate',
Basil Blackwell.
J. Cheetham (1977), 'Unwanted Pregnancy and Counselling',
Routledge & Kegan Paul.
British Association of Social Workers (1977), 'Guidelines
on Social Work with the Elderly'.
C. Rowlings (1981), 'Social Work with Elderly People',
Allen & Unwin.
E.M. Goldberg (1970), 'Helping the Aged', Allen & Unwin.
C.P. Brearley (1975), 'Social Work, Ageing and Society',
Routledge & Kegan Paul.
C.P. Brearley (1977), 'Residential Work with the Elderly',
Routledge & Kegan Paul.
L. Burton (ed.) (1975), 'Care of the Child Facing Death',
Routledge & Kegan Paul.
British Association of Social Workers (1975), 'Guidelines
for Social Workers working with Sufferers from Spina
Bifida and Hydrocephalus'.
Central Council for the Education and Training in Social
Work (1974), 'People with handicaps need Better Trained
Workers'.

Chapter 5

Symptoms

INTRODUCTION

The word 'symptom' derived from Greek signifies a fall or a
misfortune. A symptom is defined in the 'OED' as: 'A
(bodily or mental) phenomenon, circumstance or change in
condition arising from or accompanying a disease or affliction, and constituting an indication or evidence of it.'

Symptoms indicate a disturbance in what is regarded as
normal and so they invariably reflect some distress.
Implicit in the concept of a symptom is the range in the
nature of the disturbance and in the amount of distress.
Both these factors are demonstrated by the symptoms discussed in this chapter.

Symptoms in themselves are merely signals indicating
that something is out of order: they do not tell what it is
that is wrong. Responding effectively to a symptom entails
reaching an understanding about its underlying causes by
means of a differential diagnosis. Attempts at this are a
central feature of both medicine and social work, although
the processes involved in each are in some ways very different as Chapter 2 indicates.

The fundamental importance of diagnostic understanding
as a preliminary to treatment/helping is implicit, if not
explicit, in the discussion of all symptoms in this chapter.
The causes of pain are multiple; breathlessness can be due
to a very large number of different reasons and the same is
true of restricted mobility; the causes of loneliness,
anxiety and depression, which are largely subjective conditions, are as varied as is human nature itself.

The strong emphasis, so far, on the importance of diagnosis as a necessary prerequisite to responding to symptoms

needs some modification, however. Given the fact that
there is a general tendency in human life for problems to
outstrip the availability of solutions, the causes of some
symptoms remain unknown, however careful and thorough
the work of diagnosis. But in situations of this kind it is
often possible to provide relief of symptoms without a clear
understanding of why particular measures are successful.
For example, some of the recent controversy over the use
of electroconvulsive therapy in psychiatric illness has highlighted both its effectiveness in certain types of depression
and the absence of knowledge as to how it works.

Medicine has always relied heavily on 'symptomatic treatments', i.e. on providing treatments of symptoms the causes
of which were not known by means of remedies which have
proved effective for reasons not understood. Some, like
digitalis, have proved to have a clear physiological action
after they have long been used empirically. Others, for
which no such action can be demonstrated, illustrate the
important part played in health and disease by human
emotions. It is most probably this factor which explains
why faith and hope can invest therapeutically neutral treatments with strong therapeutic effects. Such treatments are
called 'placebos' and their value should not be underestima-
ted. Perhaps the most important single aspect of this
phenomenon is that it demonstrates the importance in healing work of all kinds, including both medicine and social
work, of a constructive relationship between the helper and
the person being helped; within this trust and hope nour-
ished by care and concern can function. At its best such a
relationship can in itself provide relief and comfort, if not
cure, without a need to resort to placebos.

PAIN

In one of its many forms this symptom will be familiar to
many readers. At one extreme it is part of normal life –
everybody pricks their finger, pulls a muscle, has an occasional headache, toothache or indigestion pain. At the
other extreme it is an obvious signal of serious disease and
injury: the pain of a kidney stone or a coronary thrombosis,
or a broken large bone, can be so overwhelming as to dominate the mind and exclude almost every other thought or
feeling. In between these extremes, the pain of childbirth
can be severe, but must count as part of normal life.

Is there such a thing as mental pain? In one sense all pain is mental. It may come from a damaged toe or a diseased lung, but it is experienced by the mind. But there is a kind of pain which is experienced by the severely depressed person which does not have its origin in any bodily organ, unless it be brain and central nervous system, but which, if the depression is severe enough, actually feels like pain. This rather extreme example highlights the fact that no pain is a purely physiological phenomenon. As will be seen later, its manifestations, intensity and effects on the individual concerned are greatly influenced by that individual's personality and his social and cultural milieu.

People describe pain to doctors using different words: ache, spasm, knife-like, boring, sickening pain. They associate it with something they do: 'It comes on when I take a breath or cough' - as in cases of pleurisy, a pulled chest muscle or a broken rib; 'It gets better when I lie on the floor' - low backache due to a prolapsed intervertebral disc; 'It is relieved when I drink milk' - when there is a gastric or duodenal ulcer; 'Pain killers don't help' - if headache is caused by anxiety. All these descriptions and associated features are extremely helpful to the process of disentangling the source and cause of the pain when this is not immediately obvious.

Some people have to live with pain for a large part of their life: a person with rheumatoid arthritis or an old injury which cannot be healed are examples. Does it trouble them less through sheer habit? One certainly meets people who maintain that they have got used to living with pain, but there are others who say: 'It's worse than it ever was, I can't stand it'.

It seems that earlier and more successful treatment of many diseases has reduced the number of those in the population who have chronic pain, although it would be difficult to produce figures to prove this. There are now very few people who cannot be reassured that a way of relieving their pain for most of the time is both available and will be put at their disposal.

The mechanism of pain

Pain is felt by the mind, but how does it originate and how does it reach the mind?

Certain parts of the body are capable of producing pain, others are not, regardless of what is done to them.   The skin is the most obvious example of a part capable of producing pain: it will do so if squeezed, scraped, cut or exposed to extremes of temperature.   This is so because it contains end-organs of the nervous system which react to any of these assaults by relaying a signal to the brain through the connection of peripheral nerves and spinal cord.   Some end-organs only relay a sensation of pain; others are capable of relaying sensations of heat and cold, but not the pain which attaches to their extremes, there are others which relay the sense of being touched.   Nervous connections are in the first place to a lower part of the brain called the thalamus, which is chiefly responsible for the 'feeling' element in the sensations conveyed, but there are further connections to the higher part, the cerebral cortex, which is chiefly responsible for discriminating where a pain comes from or how severe it is.

Pain can come from some internal organs, but not all. The outer covering of the lung ('pleura') gives pain if inflamed or cut and this is felt when breathing.   The heart gives pain if its muscle is damaged as, for instance, when part of its own blood supply is cut off by a clot in a coronary artery.   The intestine gives rise to pain if its hollow tube is stretched too much or if it contracts a segment too fiercely.   But the tissue of the lung itself or of the liver, apart from its outer covering, does not give rise to pain, whatever happens to it.

As already mentioned in Chapter 4, referred pain is an important phenomenon in medicine.   It can occur in any part of the body and can be distinguished from pain at the actual site of injury or disease – an important diagnostic variable.

One can think of pain as not dissimilar to a telephone system.   Dialling a number in a house causes a bell to ring in a central exchange or another house.   Pricking a finger causes pain in the brain and the mind.   It is therefore not surprising that pain can be elicited by electrical stimulation of the surface of the brain itself and the pain may seem to come from the hand or the foot, depending on which point of the surface is stimulated.

Which illnesses are painful and which are not?

It is possible, and not even rare, to suffer from cancer and die from it without having pain and without needing medicines directly aimed at relieving pain. It is equally true that cancer, particularly in its later stages, can cause severe pain. The variation depends in part on where in the body the growth or its secondary deposits are sited: for instance, cancer in the bone is painful and in the liver it is not. There must be other factors involved as well, but their nature is as yet not understood.

It is not surprising that diseases or injuries which involve pressure on physical nerves, or an irritation or destruction of them, should be painful. This explains the pain of lumbago, sciatica, or a 'disc'. Pain-conveying nerves must, by definition, be involved in any painful condition, but as we have already pointed out, pain end-organs do not exist in every part of the body.

Typically painful conditions are the following earache (otitis media), a boil, and a toothache, where stretching of tissues or swelling within a confined space are the immediate cause of pain; pleurisy, where two surfaces which normally slide smoothly on each other in the act of breathing become inflamed and roughened and create a grating; the pain of inflamed joints must arise in a similar fashion and arthritis certainly counts among the more painful disorders.

The pain of coronary heart disease – angina and coronary thrombosis – ('heart attack') is more difficult to explain. It appears to be due to the heart muscle being short of oxygen. In angina this occurs when physical exertion raises the requirement of oxygen and the coronary arteries, being narrowed or blocked, cannot convey what is needed quickly enough. In a coronary thrombosis there is a sudden blockage of a coronary artery by clotting of blood and this cuts off oxygen completely, resulting not only in pain, but also in damage or destruction in the part of the heart muscle which the blocked artery normally supplies.

Colic is that particular spasmodic sort of pain which arises in hollow tubes, notably the intestine, the duct of the gall-bladder and the ducts from the kidneys to the urinary bladder (the ureters). This pain seems to result from a stretching or contraction of muscle against unusual resistance, for instance, an impacted stone. Though seldom of a long duration, the pain can be extremely severe.

Examples of diseases which either cause no pain at all or

very little are bronchitis, asthma and hepatitis (inflammation of the liver or 'infectious jaundice'). They do, however, cause other forms of suffering. On the whole, it
must be said that it is far more difficult to think of examples
of diseases which cause no pain than of those which do.

Does pain serve a purpose?

Purpose is a problematic word in biology – indeed in any
science – because the scientific method of thinking throws
little or no light on purposes. One does not have to be a
scientist, however, to see the value of pain as a signal that
something is wrong and as a stimulus to remedial action.
Unfortunately, pain so often outlives its usefulness in these
respects and becomes totally disadvantageous. It is often
claimed that pain draws out in its sufferers the finer qualities of human nature: whilst this is sometimes true, it is
equally true that pain can demoralise. Illich has argued (1)
that without an experience of pain human beings would be
incapable of experiencing pleasure.

The relief of pain

It is a general belief in our society that pain should be
relieved whenever possible. There are some people who
believe that it is right to put up with a certain amount of
pain and who are therefore reluctant to seek relief: 'I don't
believe in taking aspirin for a slight headache'. The
majority do not refuse help, however, when faced with a
really severe pain, and very few carry their objections to
pain relief to a point where they take unnecessary risks.
More prevalent currently is the attitude that no physical
discomfort, however minor, should be tolerated. At its
extreme, this can lead to an excessive reliance on analgesics, even to the point of addiction. Women who are housebound on account of having young children, or who lack
sufficient outlet for their interests, may suffer from a sense
of lack of personal fulfilment and as a result are particularly vulnerable in this respect.
   Most pains can be relieved. Medicine directs its efforts
to removing the cause of pain, when possible: letting out
the pus, extracting the tooth, destroying with an antibiotic
the bacteria which cause pleurisy or otitis media. When

cure in this sense is impossible, there is a range of symptomatic relief for pain.   Aspirin or paracetamol are the
commonest remedies which people will try first.   In this
country, in order to obtain anything more potent, a doctor's
prescription is needed, and for good reasons.   No drug
suits everyone and many have undesirable side-effects in
certain people or when taken in too great quantity.   This is
true of even aspirin and paracetamol.   When it comes to
the really strong analgesics, such as heroin and morphia,
there are not only side-effects, but also the added danger
of addiction - physical dependence so great that the drug
must be continued and the dose increased.   Clearly, therefore, accuracy in dosage to ensure adequate relief without
danger is crucial.

No drug used in the relief of pain lasts longer than a few
hours before it is broken down chemically by the body and
loses its effect.   In cases of persistent pain it must therefore be repeated constantly.   This is usually most conven-
iently done by taking the drug by mouth.   Injections act
more quickly and do not affect digestion (which some drugs
do when taken by mouth); but they usually require someone
else to administer them and so tend to be used only in cases
of most intractable pain.

The psycho-social aspects of pain

Although, when viewed from a biological perspective, pain
results from tissue damage and is mediated by the nervous
system of the body, it can also be profitably regarded as an
aspect of a more basic human experience, namely that of
suffering.   This is an even more elusive concept than pain,
but what can be said about suffering with certainty is that it
is a universal phenomenon rooted in human existence itself.

The actual degree of suffering and its manifestations is
influenced by many different factors, of which physical pain
is but one.   Some writers on pain, for example Szasz, (2)
argue that there are two distinct 'languages of pain'.   One
is the 'language of physical pain' used in scientifically
oriented medicine; it emphasises the objective, physiological aspects of pain.   The other is the 'language of psychological pain' used in psycho-dynamically oriented medicine,
which views pain as a largely subjective experience and a
form of non-verbal communication intended to draw attention
to a perceived threat to one's proper integrity as a person.

The psychodynamic view of pain acknowledges the influence of personal social and cultural factors as well as of the biological ones.   It thus provides a justification for using the terms 'pain' and 'suffering' interchangeably.   It is such a view which seems implicit in the following statement by Dubos: 'Clearly health and disease cannot be defined merely in terms of anatomical, physiological and mental attributes. Their real measure is the ability of the individual to function in a manner acceptable to himself and the group of which he is a part.' (3)   One cannot but deduce from this statement that failure to function in such an 'acceptable manner' leads to pain.

Montaigne, the French essayist of the sixteenth century, must have had considerable insight into the influence upon pain of the various non-biological factors to have written the following:

We suffer more from one touch of the barber-surgeon's knife than from ten blows of a sword sustained in the heat of a battle.   The pains of confinement inflicted by the physicians and by God are considered by us severe and are thought to call for all sorts of ceremonies; but there are whole nations which pay no attention to these pains – behind the Swiss infantry you find marching wives round whose necks infants born yesterday are suspended (quoted in Merskey and Spear (4)).

In their extensive study of the subject, Merskey and Spear have found that the incidence of pain among a group of psychiatric patients was particularly heavy.   The most common forms of pain among this group were headaches, and gastric and cardiac pain.   Patients who were diagnosed as suffering from anxiety were the group most prone to complain of pain; those suffering from depression came next. Pain occurred most commonly in men in Social Class V but it was not related to social class in female patients.

These findings are thought to indicate not that psychiatric patients and people in the disadvantaged social classes are necessarily less resistant to pain, but that they have a greater need to resort to pain as a medium of communication.   The reason for this lies in their restricted ability to use other media of communication, particularly that of language, due to both their limited articulateness and the social distance between them and their doctors.   The validity of this hypothesis seems to be confirmed by the observation that readiness to complain in a direct fashion about emotional difficulties is much greater in upper income groups and among better-educated persons than among working-class people. Merskey and Spear explain this as follows: 'Pain will tend to be preferred by these groups /i.e. working class/ because it has a greater communication value and because it does not depend on sophisticated understanding either by the patient, the doctor, or the rest of society.' It is worth remembering in this context that, as mentioned in Chapter 4, children also resort frequently to pain as a means of communicating various forms of psychological distress. This too can be understood in terms of both limitations in the use of language and the social distance between children and adults.

Other important findings in this area include the relationship between various social and ethnic factors and the differences in both pain perception thresholds (i.e. points at which a sensation begins to be felt as painful) and pain reaction thresholds (i.e. points at which pain is found unbearable). Both these were found to be lower in women than in men, but no significant differences attributable to age were found. Several North American studies have shown Negroes to have lower pain thresholds than Whites; pain thresholds of Canadians of Jewish and French origins were found to be lower than those of Anglo-Saxon stock. Miners were found to have higher than average threholds.

These and similar findings appear to indicate the important part played by cultural factors in determining attitudes towards pain. In this context, the now classic study by Zborowski (5) deserves particular mention. He studied four groups of patients in an American Veterans' Hospital: those of Jewish, Italian and Irish origins, and those whom he described as 'old Americans'. Zborowski found the following striking differences in the reactions to pain by members of these four groups. Both the Italian and the Jewish patients showed the strongest reactions, but there were significant differences in the nature of these reactions. The Italians were mostly concerned about the here and now impact of the pain whilst the Jews were worried about its future implications. As a result, Jewish patients were much less responsive to reassurance and to pain-killing drugs than were the Italians. The 'old Americans' tended to minimise pain, they disliked 'fuss' and they shied off any 'emotionalisation' of pain altogether; their future orientation, unlike that of the Jewish patients, was one of optimism. The Irish patients were able to accept a great deal of pain and they showed a stoical attitude towards it. This acceptance of pain, unlike that of the 'old Americans', reflected however, a fatalistic view of it as inevitable.

Zborowski considers these different reactions, particularly those concerned with the time oreintation (whether it is towards the past, the future or the present) to be closely related to the different child-rearing practices in the four cultures. This finding makes an interesting comparison with the discovery by the Newsons in this country, (6) in the course of their research into the child-rearing practices in families of different social origins, that attitudes towards punishment differed significantly. The relevance of childhood experiences to later attitudes towards pain was also highlighted in a study quoted by Merskey and Spear (7) which had revealed that a group of particularly pain-prone patients had had punitive or abusive parents.

The social worker and pain

A view of pain which extends it beyond the purely physiological and which equates it with suffering must lead to the conclusion that social workers are constantly in the business of handling pain. Their awareness that pain may be resorted to as the only effective means of communication should make them more sensitive in responding to this form of non-verbal communication by clients with a variety of problems. The value of such a response is further enhanced in those situations where people lack adequate understanding from doctors if their 'organic orientation' leads them to underestimate the significance of pain unrelated to physical damage or disease.

A major reason for the frequency of social workers' encounters with pain lies in the extent of the economic, social, familial and psychological stresses experienced by their clients. These result in varying degrees of suffering and in different manifestations of it, but its total absence is extremely rare.

Paradoxically social workers will be effective in responding to pain only if they subscribe to a philosophy of suffering which accepts it as an integral part of human existence, yet is not complacent towards it when it can be prevented, cured or alleviated. There is doubtless truth in Illich's assertion that 'only pain perceived as curable is intolerable'. (8)

BREATHLESSNESS

Breathlessness 'may be due to any condition which renders
the blood impure or deficient in oxygen, and which therefore produces excessive involuntary efforts to gain more
air' ('Black's Medical Dictionary').   Thus the word is an
umbrella term covering a wide range of conditions giving
rise to the same symptom.   This is important for social
workers to realise because the underlying cause of breathlessness plays an important part in determining what particular social and emotional connotations should be their primary concern.   An essential prerequisite therefore to being
able to work intelligently and helpfully with a client is for
social workers to acquaint themselves with the relevant
medical facts.   This they can best achieve by obtaining
information from the client's doctor, usually the general
practitioner, but, where appropriate, the hospital specialist.
    The significance of the term 'breathlessness' lies in the
fact that it has certain common features regardless of its
particular causes.   Shortage of air for breathing is the
major one of these.   If severe, this gives rise to very unpleasant and frightening sensations.   What must be appreciated is the close association between breathing and living;
breathlessness can lead to feelings of apprehension about
death which are out of proportion to the existing physiological limitation.   According to the views of a number of
dynamic psychologists, the emotional significance of
breathlessness is further increased by the fact that it reac-
tivates the so called 'birth trauma' in the memory of the
individual.   The original experience of biological and psychological shock on the emergence of the newly born from
the protected environment of the maternal uterus into the
outside world was accompanied by feelings of utter helplessness and panic.   These feelings may be reactivated on any
subsequent occasion reminiscent of the original experience.
While this particular view of the cause of the emotional component in breathlessness is controversial and largely
beyond proof, what cannot be denied is the strength of this
element in many breathless people.   The panic experienced
in the course of an asthmatic attack is perhaps the clearest
illustration of this, but it is by no means unique.
    The relationship between breathlessness and emotional
states is not only in one direction; not only can breathlessness cause emotional reactions, it can also result from it.

This is well known, for example, among actors, for whom breathlessness is a common experience in 'stage fright'. The association is reflected in commonly used expressions such as 'it took my breath away' to reflect shock. Social workers frequently meet clients who are in an overwrought state, and since this may manifest itself among other forms in breathlessness, the presence of this symptom in an interview can therefore provide a useful pointer to the extent to which the client is upset. Nervousness at the beginning of an important interview with a stranger is common (although, before a client's breathlessness is attributed to this, it is important to make sure that he has not hurried to be on time or had to climb many stairs!); as the discussion continues, the points at which the client becomes short of breath can have considerable significance. Awareness of this is of value in terms of both understanding the client and his problems and of handling his feelings so as to avoid causing unnecessary distress.

When one looks more closely, one finds that the symptom of breathlessness does not always have the same characteristics. It can take the form of distressed breathing with a crowing hoarse sound on breathing in, as in croup (laryngitis) in young children. It can take the form of wheezing, a musical sound like organ pipes, to be heard in asthma, especially in breathing out. It can be a distressed panting as in pneumonia or heart failure. Finally it can be a feeling described by the patient but not usually visible: 'I can't get enough air', 'I can't fill my lungs deep enough'. This form of breathlessness is always associated with tiredness or anxiety and does not represent a disease of heart or lungs, or even anaemia.

The major causes of breathlessness can be divided into four groups: disorders of the air passages and lungs, those of the heart, anaemia, and tiredness or emotional distress To understand the relationship between these conditions and the symptoms, one needs to know something of the relevant anatomy, physiology and pathology.

The anatomy and physiology of breathing

The act of breathing is controlled by a particular area of the brain near the neck and is normally unconscious. This part of the brain controls the rhythmical movements of the chest wall and diaphragm which expand the lungs to draw in

air through the mouth, nose, throat, larynx, the central
windpipe (trachea) and the tubes which branch out from it
into many smaller units – like a tree turned upside down
(the bronchial tubes). It is the elasticity of the lungs
themselves which causes air to be expelled as the chest
wall ceases to exert its pull (expiration).

The main function of the lungs in relation to breathing is
exchange of gases between air and blood. At the end of the
smallest branches of the bronchial tree are microscopic
sacs called alveoli. These have thin walls in which run
the smallest branches of the arteries and veins. The walls
are so thin that gases can permeate them in both directions.
Oxygen enters the blood from the air and carbon dioxide, a
waste product, enters the air from the blood.

The blood which arrives in the walls of the alveoli is
lacking in oxygen, as it comes from the rest of the body
where oxygen has been used up. It picks up oxygen from
the air and conveys it via the heart to the tissues of all the
organs of the body.

In the tissues the blood stream is again divided into
microscopically small tubes called capillaries which are
capable of being permeated by gases. A similar exchange
takes place there as in the lungs. The tissues take up
oxygen from the blood and the blood takes up waste products,
including carbon dioxide, from the tissues.

Blood consists of fluid (plasma) and cells (corpuscles).
It is the red corpuscles which convey oxygen and carbon
dioxide.

The heart pumps the blood to the tissues. It has a left
side and a right side – separated from each other. The
chambers on the left side expel blood to the tissues when
the powerful muscle of the heart contracts. The chambers
on the right side expel blood to the lungs. Blood which has
gone there returns through the veins of each lung to enter
the left side of the heart and to be pumped to the rest of the
body, carrying oxygen in red corpuscles. When the blood
has passed through the tissues of the body and unloaded its
oxygen, it is returned to the right side of the heart through
the veins. The chemical in red corpuscles which carries
oxygen is haemoglobin: when loaded with oxygen it gives a
bright red colour to the blood (arterial blood – because it
travels in the arteries from the heart and tissues); when
loaded with waste products and devoid of oxygen, it gives a
blueish colour (venous blood).

Breathlessness due to disease of the respiratory organs

Obstruction to the airways is the most obvious cause for breathlessness. This can occur at the larynx, as in children who have 'croup', or in the bronchial tubes, as in asthma or bronchitis. In both these conditions the bronchial tubes are narrowed because of mucus collecting or because of spasm of the muscular walls of the tubes giving rise to high or low pitched 'wheezing'. Other obvious reasons for breathlessness are when one lung has been removed in order to get rid of a growth, or when there is fluid in the pleural cavity between lung and chest wall, compressing the lung. When a plug of mucus or the presence of a growth obstructs one sizeable bronchial tube, the lung beyond the obstruction becomes airless. Here again breathlessness is a logical consequence.

Breathlessness due to heart disease

If the heart fails to act as an efficient pump, breathlessness is the most important symptom, whatever the reason for this failure. It is basically due to a slowing up of the circulation through lungs and tissues with resulting defects in the exchange of gases. Exactly how this results in breathlessness is less easy to see than in the case of lung disease.

There are a number of common reasons why the heart can fail as a pump. The pressure against which it has to work may become too great. In 'high blood pressure' an unknown cause makes the small blood vessels throughout much of the body contract, so squeezing the blood back and requiring greater work by the heart to force it through. Similar overload may result from narrowed or leaking valves in the heart itself. Alternatively the muscle of the heart may itself weaken as in 'coronary artery disease', where the calibre of the blood vessels which bring oxygen to the muscle of the heart is diminished through thickening and roughening of the walls of the vessels ('atherosclerosis'). High blood pressure and coronary artery disease now account for the highest incidence of illness, incapacity and deaths from heart disease.

Breathlessness due to anaemia

Anaemia means a reduction in the amount of haemoglobin in the red corpuscles and therefore a reduced capacity for carrying oxygen. This in turn leads to a deficiency in the supply of oxygen to the heart muscle and breathlessness results. Anaemia has to be fairly severe (below three-quarters of the normal amount of haemoglobin) before breath-lessness is noticed.

There are many causes and manifestations of anaemia; their recognition and differentiation call for considerable expertise. It is not possible to diagnose anaemia merely from a person's appearance. Many people have pale com-plexions without being anaemic. The only reliable way of detecting it is to send blood to a laboratory for analysis. An analysis of a sample – 'the blood count' – goes far towards establishing the type of anaemia.

The important common types of anaemia are those due to blood loss, to lack of iron and to lack of vitamin B12. The last two are very easy to treat successfully. The treatment of anaemia due to blood loss calls for prior identification of where and why blood is being lost. For example, this may be due to such different causes as peptic ulceration, haemorrhoids or, in women fibroid tumours in the uterus.

In addition to these three common types of anaemia there are, however, a large number of others much less well understood as, for example, when haemoglobin is destroyed inside the body (haemolytic anaemia). It is because anaemias are such a complex group of diseases that haema-tology has become established as a special branch of medicine.

Breathlessness due to tiredness or emotional distress

The physiology of breathlessness due to psychological fac-tors is much less clear. Breathlessness in these emotional states is, however, undoubtedly related to upsets in the autonomic nervous system which controls the actions of the circulatory and the digestive systems and which is normally outside conscious control. It consists of two sub-systems: the sympathetic nervous system and the parasympathetic nervous system. The first of these inhibits the action of the intestines and augments the action of the heart and the second does the reverse. The function of these two systems is to prepare the body to respond defensively to danger and to maintain a state of homeostasis by regulating the action of respiration, digestion, excretion and vaso-motor control. When an individual's emotional state is in any way disturbed, this results in a mobilisation of the autonomic nervous system for defensive action. If the need for this is prolonged or occurs too frequently, physiological damage to the organs involved may follow – this is the dynamic behind psychosomatic disease, discussed in Chapter 3.

Helping people who suffer from breathlessness

Breathlessness due to disorders of the air passages and lungs

Within this group chronic bronchitis, asthma, pneumonia and cancers of the bronchus and the lungs are the most common conditions. In some areas the various industrial diseases affecting the lungs, such as pneumoconiosis and asbestosis, are important.

Chronic bronchitis provides a good illustration of an ill-ness in which the degree of incapacity can vary enormously. At one extreme are people who believe that their 'smoker's cough' is normal. The next stage is when people are par-ticularly susceptible to chest infections and take a long time to recover from them, but otherwise can function relatively unimpeded. They may require help from a social worker with a change of employment if they are working in the open air or in conditions where they are exposed to dust and fumes, or with rehousing if their current accommodation is damp and cold. As the condition progresses, the person concerned becomes increasingly breathless and incapable of physical exertion. Even a relatively light job may become unmanageable, especially if getting to it entails a long or uncomfortable journey. If people who become afflicted in this way are in their fifties, finding an alterna-tive job may well present considerable difficulties (even when there is no mass unemployment as at present), and so the client may be faced with the problem of unemployment and all the consequences, including a sudden drop in income and a loss of self-esteem. There are few conditions as distressing as chronic bronchitis in its final stages. The patient is constantly short of air and is often gasping for breath. He (or she) is incapable of the slightest exertion: not only is the taking of a few steps from one chair to the next, or to reach the lavatory, beyond his physical capacity, talking too can become an effort beyond endurance: the person is dying of slow suffocation.

Men tend to be more frequently affected by chronic bronchitis and allied chest conditions than women (although there is some evidence that the position is changing with the increase of cigarette smoking among women). Where the medical condition has reached the point at which the patient is no longer capable of fulfilling his breadwinning role, his wife has to assume this or, if she had worked before, become the primary provider. In either event the effect on the self-image of the patient is likely to be considerable. If the marital relationship is particularly vulnerable to major adaptations of this kind, or has been built on a strong dependence on the afflicted partner by the other, these changes in balance can be a threat to both husband and wife, and impose additional demands on them. Where there are adolescent children in the household their needs may not be met, especially the need of adolescent boys to derive an adequate model of masculinity as a basis for future functioning.

Successful adaptation to such family problems calls for a great deal of mutual understanding and tolerance on the part of those concerned. It can be made even harder by some of the personality changes which often accompany distressing chronic conditions of this nature.

Although there is no adequate documentation at present, social workers experienced in working with patients suffering from severe chronic bronchitis, have found that these gradually develop certain character traits, in particular becoming excessively demanding and nagging, as well as misanthropic. This makes their company increasingly hard to tolerate for those who are in constant touch with them. It is this, more than any other single factor, which accounts for the frequency of acute marital disharmony in the families of these patients.

There is great opportunity for social workers, whatever the original reason for their involvement, to attempt to relieve family tensions and to raise the level of tolerance and contentment. Individual interviews, joint interviews with both partners, family group sessions, or a mixture of all these methods can be used as appropriate. The objective is to enable to family members to express their ambiva-

lent feelings towards each other and their resentment of
the hard circumstances of their lives. This can both
alleviate current suffering and prevent future complications
which might arise from unresolved feelings of this nature.

Breathlessness due to heart disease

The range and the extent of disability produced by a malfunctioning heart is very wide. There have, however,
been some important developments in recent years. For
example, some congenital heart defects, such as those
causing 'blue babies', led in the past to severe disablement
and often to death. With the advent of the heart-lung
machine many of these conditions are now treated very
successfully by surgery.

The prevalence of rheumatic heart disease is now much
diminished. It is caused by a malfunctioning of one or
more of the valves in the heart which results from inflammatory changes following on acute rheumatic fever. It
was usually found in relatively young people, especially
women, many of whom were mothers of young children, and
was a steadily progressive condition. The fact that
rheumatic heart disease is no longer a major cause of
handicap and death in young and middle-aged adults is due
both to a much lower incidence of acute rheumatism and its
secondary effects, and to modern surgical treatment which
is often very effective. Where this disease is still encountered, the degree of breathlessness experienced by the
patient is directly related to the amount of valvular damage
and to the amount of exertion expended. One of the important tasks facing social workers with clients in this group
is therefore to help them to avoid excessive physical
strains. This is often far from easy, not only because of
material and other external constraints, but also because
there is a psychological reluctance to accept the reality of
a severe handicap at a relatively young age. Mothers of
young children, for example, may experience considerable
guilt at being unable to play with them - an activity which
they associate with good mothering. This may lead to a
paradoxical situation in which these women feel miserable
when their physical condition is relatively sound as a result
of rest, and feel happier and more contented when in a state
of physical exhaustion as a result of having 'overdone'
things. Very skilful social work is needed to help such

people modify their values towards recognising that their
worth to their families lies primarily in what they represent
in themselves rather than in the specific activities they
carry out.

Coronary heart disease (which is due to narrowing of the
blood vessels within the muscle of the heart itself) is usually
an illness of middle age and old age. It varies greatly in
intensity, in pattern and in duration. The chief symptom
is chest pain, but this is often accompanied by breathlessness, and, in older age groups, replaced by it. Pain is
typically associated with frequent exertion (angina pectoris).
When it occurs at rest it is of more serious significance and,
if severe, may mean that thrombosis is occurring in a
coronary artery with damage to the heart muscle and the
risk of death.

When the heart muscle is weakened, whether by coronary
disease or any of the other causes of 'heart failure', there
may be other manifestations than breathlessness, e.g. the
accumulation of surplus fluid.

Coronary heart disease may spare its victims for many
years or may cause instant death. It is of all illnesses the
least predictable. Medical or surgical interventions can
play a part depending on the particular symptoms, severity
and pattern of complications. The relationship between the
cause and onset of the disease and psychological stress is
still disputed, whereas its relationship to cigarette smoking
is established. Once present there is no doubt that psychological factors become important.

Social-work intervention must be based on a keen appreciation of these facts. The easing of a patient's mind and
help with problems of daily living can actively contribute to
the management of the disease.

A feature of heart disease which should not be overlooked
relates to the symbolic meanings with which the heart has
been credited. A brief acquaintance with literature will
show that it is regarded as the seat of love, loyalty and
courage. People have therefore a great investment in its
'health', which is reinforced by the close association of the
heart with life itself. Until very recently death was
equated with the cessation of heart beats and although in
medicine the concept of 'brain death' has replaced that of
'heart stoppage', this shift of emphasis is not likely to have
much effect for some time on the popular perception of the
heart as the supreme organ. The prevalence in our society
of coronary thrombosis, one of the few conditions which can

result in unexpected and sudden death, is a further factor
in heart disease carrying a particular threat to many people.
For all these reasons, social workers in touch with cardiac patients must be prepared to become involved in these
patients' existential preoccupations: their fear of death,
their attempts to discover the meaning of life, and in their
need for some positive philosophy to help them face the unknown. Because of the widespread reluctance in our contemporary society to face up to these issues, many patients
will raise them indirectly and will expect some positive clue
from the social worker that the subject is not 'taboo',
before they can feel free to discuss their thoughts and feelings more explicitly.

Breathlessness due to anaemia

Anaemia is common among social workers' clients, in women
from socially deprived families and old people. Even if
only of moderate severity, it can affect people's lives considerably. Its characteristic features are a sense of
chronic tiredness and apathy, and frequent headaches,
which make coping with the demands of everyday living difficult even under the most favourable circumstances.
When, however, these circumstances are particularly difficult, as when the family budget is very tight and making
ends meet calls for exceptional ingenuity, or when housing
conditions are well below standard and add strain to the
normal demands of housework and child management, a
woman suffering from anaemia cannot but feel outfaced and
unable to cope. Her home may become neglected and her
family deprived of the attention they require. Tiredness
results in irritability and impatience, as well as in lethargy,
and the effects of this on family relationships can be severe,
the children having to resort to increasingly demanding and
difficult behaviour in order to attract attention to themselves and the husband being driven to spend his leisure
time away from home in more animated company.
Social workers may be the first people in a position to
note not only that all is not well but also the possibility that
the client is suffering from anaemia and should be encouraged to seek medical advice. This is particularly important because, as already mentioned, people from socially
disadvantaged groups are known to be slow to seek medical
help. To many of them such symptoms as constant tiredness

or chronic backache are the normal accompaniments of
living and they ignore the possibility that they may be suffering from some illness which is treatable.

On the whole, many social workers are quicker to spot
difficulties of a psychological or environmental nature than
those which derive from physical ill health. The unhelpful
and even dangerous consequences of such a bias are illustrated by the case of a client who was being seen regularly
for a period of several months by a social worker in a voluntary family agency. The assumed problem with which the
social worker was attempting to help was chronic depression. However, the client showed no improvement in spite
of the combined efforts of herself and the social worker and
the situation had reached an impasse when one day while
shopping at a supermarket, the client collapsed and was
taken to hospital. She was found to have a very severe
degree of iron deficiency anaemia!

Where a client is known to suffer from anaemia the social
worker can frequently be of considerable help by alleviating
some of the domestic burdens and by ensuring that she has
an adequate diet. Financial help needs to be reinforced by
psychological support as the mother of a family who live in
poverty may well feel guilty at having more expensive food
than the rest of the family.

Anaemia which results from malnutrition is particularly
common among old people. The unsatisfactory diet of many
old people (unsatisfactory in the sense of failure to eat the
right foods rather than in quantitative terms) is due not only
to inadequate income which can make foods rich in protein
and vitamins beyond reach, but it can also be the by-product
of some of the other problems of old age: depression leading to self-neglect, dementia, or sheer lack of physical
strength. We have already discussed the place of social
work in relation to old people's needs and problems in
Chapter 4.

Breathlessness due to tiredness or emotional distress

It is important that all alternative causes of breathlessness
are excluded before this cause is diagnosed. Once such a
diagnosis has been reached, however, the next important
step is to try to discover why a person is tired or distressed. The social worker can make a valuable contribution
in this respect: the reason may well be related to the

patient's social circumstances, whether because of their
adverse nature or his excessive reaction to them. A sense
of chronic tiredness, with distress which is disproportionate to the difficulties being experienced, is likely to reflect
anxiety, depression, or both. (Both these manifestations
of psychological states will be discussed more fully later.)

RESTRICTED MOBILITY

A person's mobility is obviously related to his age. A
healthy man or woman of 20 should be able to walk uphill or
up two flights of stairs at their normal pace without becoming breathless or having to stop for a rest. One would not
expect as much of a healthy 80-year-old. It is normal for
mobility to decrease with age since breathlessness, stiff-
ness, or weakness occur more quickly and after less exertion.

Entirely different from the age-related 'normal' reduction
in mobility is the near total immobility of someone with a
very severe joint disease or with a paralysis of nerves and
muscles affecting the arms and legs. Such cases are fortunately rare, but they may involve confinement to bed or
wheelchair and almost total helplessness and dependence on
others. A victim of such an extreme immobility will require
to be fed, washed, dressed and helped to pass water and
motions - a degree of physical attention comparable to that
which is given to a small baby.

Anatomy and physiology

Mobility depends on muscles pulling on bones and on the
joints between bones. The action of muscles depends on
their nerve-supply. Their co-ordinated action in a purposeful movement such as walking depends on the co-ordi-
nating power of the central nervous system which sends
messages to muscles via the spinal cord and the peripheral
nerves. When muscles contract, they use oxygen and
create waste products; for this a blood supply is essential.
When many muscles move, as in walking or running, the
demand for oxygen rises sharply and the heart which pumps
blood and oxygen to them has to work more vigorously; so
do the lungs. Running is therefore accompanied by an increased rate and force of the heart beat and by heavier
breathing.

Mobility will be restricted if there is any fault in bones,
joints, muscles, peripheral nerves, central nervous system,
blood, heart or lungs. Faced with a person who has
become unable to walk, a doctor may have to search for
causes in any of these organs (and, more rarely, be prepared to find a psychological cause such as a phobia).

Examples of disorders restricting mobility

Injuries

A bruised muscle may limit mobility through pain and stiff-
ness. In the case of a broken bone mobility will be limited
for much longer, the condition causing great pain on movement and weakness secondary to the pain.
     A dislocated joint, with tearing of the ligaments, also
causes great pain and any movement attempted will be
extremely limited. A sprain is a torn ligament not involving displacement of the joint.
     Injury to a peripheral nerve will put out of action those
muscles which the nerve supplies, so that they cannot be
moved. If the nerve does not recover or is not repaired,
the muscles will waste and become permanently useless.
Injury to the spinal cord – for instance at the level of the
nipples – will cause paralysis of the lower limbs and also of
the function of the bladder.

Diseases of bones and joints

Diseases of the bone are now relatively rare and so can be
ignored for the present purposes. The diseases of joints
or 'arthritis' are unfortunately widespread and cause a
great deal of crippling. Three types of arthritis occur
commonly: osteo-arthritis, rheumatoid arthritis and gout.
They share the features of pain, particularly when a joint
is moved, and swelling in and around joints. They are distinguished from each other by the number of joints affected,
by which become involved earliest, and by their appearance
and that of adjacent muscles. X-rays are an important
diagnostic aid but the most conclusive evidence comes from
blood tests which usually show abnormalities in the case of
rheumatoid arthritis and gout, but not in osteo-arthritis.
     Osteo-arthritis can scarcely be called a disease; it is a

form of degeneration and part of the normal process of
ageing.   It usually affects one or two joints, particularly
those which are subject to most heavy use: the hips, the
knees and the basal joints of the thumbs.   It is not unusual
to find evidence of osteo-arthritis on an X-ray when there
have been no symptoms; symptoms most commonly come and
go.   No means of prevention is known, but symptoms can be
considerably helped by rest and by drugs; also by heat and
active exercises after the acute stage is passed.   When
pain is both severe and persistent, surgery now offers lasting help; the diseased hip joint is replaced by one made of
metal or plastic.

Rheumatoid arthritis is a disease affecting many joints.
It typically starts in the small joints of the hands and is
accompanied by a feeling of illness.   Its course is intermittent, but often progressive, deforming and crippling.
It is fortunately far less common than osteo-arthritis.   A
number of drugs relieve the symptoms, shorten acute episodes and reduce damage.   There is no single drug which
controls the disease in every sufferer.

Gout usually starts by affecting the joints of the big toe
and is extremely painful.   It is associated with an increase
in the level of uric acid in the blood and once detected, is
the easiest of the three arthritic disorders to relieve.   The
idea that it is associated with rich living is no longer
believed to be valid.

The term 'arthritis of the spine' is sometimes used.   It
usually refers to the condition 'spondylosis' involving an
increase in the size of the joint tissues in the spine; there
is a rare disorder 'ankylosing spondylosis' in which the
spinal joints eventually become fused leaving the person
with a strikingly bent posture.   More common is the simple
spondylosis which in many ways resembles osteo-arthritis
in other joints.   This is important and needs special mention because of the anatomy of the spinal joints.   They lie
next to and surround the nerves which emerge from the
spinal cord to supply every part of the body.   The nerves
are therefore vulnerable to changes in these joints.
Spondylosis commonly sets up a 'referred' pain through
pressure on a particular spinal nerve root.   The pain is
felt in the distribution of the nerve.   The commonest
example is 'sciatica' to which reference was made in
Chapter 4, but similar pains can occur anywhere from the
head downwards.   The term 'neuralgia' is sometimes used
to indicate pain of this nature: it may be felt at the back of

the head, in an arm, round the chest or abdomen, or down the leg. 'Lumbago' is another term used to describe some of these pains.

'Prolapsed disc' – another common cause of 'referred' pain – was also discussed in Chapter 4. It is often extremely difficult to distinguish spondylosis, i.e. degenerative disorder of the spine, from a 'prolapsed disc' because these two conditions are closely related both anatomically and causally.

One common disorder is sometimes incorrectly described as 'arthritis of the shoulder'. Pain on movement of the shoulder, particularly in raising the arm sideways or putting the hand behind the head, is usually due to a fault in the muscle–tendons which move the shoulder joint and the upper arm, and not to disease in the joint itself. The tendon most commonly affected by a degenerative process is the tendon of the supraspinatus muscle – hence the term 'supraspinatus tendinitis' which is applied to the condition. Another technical name given to it is 'rotator cuff lesion'.

Diseases of the muscles

Primary disorders of muscle are rare and difficult to diagnose. Perhaps the commonest is 'polymyalgia rheumatica', a condition only seen in older people. Its early detection is very worthwhile because it usually responds dramatically to treatment with steroids (cortisone).

Diseases of the peripheral nerves, spinal cord and central nervous system

This important group of disorders comprising much of the speciality of neurology, affects mobility chiefly through weakness or paralysis rather than pain. The nearer the fault to the muscle, the more it will result in a loss of power combined with wasting of that muscle; the further from the muscle (i.e. the higher in the nervous system), the more likely the loss of control and of co-ordination of whole groups of muscles. In either case weakness and paralysis may be associated with loss of sensation and changes in the reflexes. It is not difficult to distinguish neurological disorders from disorders of joints, although as indicated in the previous section, a disordered spinal joint can cause a neurological problem.

Disorder of all the peripheral nerves - peripheral neuritis - is rare. It is characterised by weakness and wasting of muscles in the hands and feet accompanied by loss of sensation. One of its many causes is a deficiency of vitamin B - familiar in Japanese prisoner-of-war camps in the Second World War. Disorders of a single nerve are much more common - particularly of the median nerve which supplies most of the small muscles of the hand. This nerve is vulnerable as it passes through a narrow entrance to the hand at the wrist - the 'carpel tunnel'. When the wrist relaxes and drops during sleep, the median nerve is easily compressed at this point, so the typical symptom is weakness and numbness of the hand on waking, with rapid improvement as the hand is moved and used.

At the other end of a peripheral nerve - near its emergence from the spinal cord - compression frequently occurs in the aperture at each side of the vertebra, as is described in the section on spondylosis above.

Poliomyelitis is an infection of the peripheral nerves, due to a specific virus attacking the nerve-cells of the motor nerves which control muscles. It is now rare in this country. The main reason for mentioning it is that it serves as one of the best examples of a disease which can be almost totally eradicated by routine immunisation of children.

Disorders of the spinal cord such as spondylosis can compress the spinal cord as well as the nerves which emerge from it. This usually occurs only in old people and at the level of the neck. It accounts for some of the weakness and unsteadiness in walking which old people describe.

Multiple sclerosis is predominantly an affliction of the spinal cord, although it also affects the optic nerve, and, at a late stage, parts of the brain. It is a disease of which the cause is still unknown and it runs a fluctuating course for many years. Each episode leaves more impairment than the last, so that an overall deterioration is the rule and death occurs due to a combination of weakness and recurrent infections of the lungs, the urinary tract or a bedsore. Increasing evidence that multiple sclerosis has an indirect relationship to a virus infection has so far not provided any basis for prevention or effective treatment. There are, however, drugs which relieve some of the symptoms in some patients.

At the onset the disease is usually characterised by

episodes of weakness in the lower limbs; this is followed
by gradual loss of control of the bladder, the upper limbs
and lastly, speech.   In its early stages, multiple sclerosis
is not easy to diagnose, and it is particularly important to
exclude other disorders which resemble it but which can be
treated successfully, such as a subacute combined degeneration of the cord, a disease related to pernicious anaemia
and reversible by the use of vitamin b12 and Folic Acid.

The later stages of multiple sclerosis are very distressing: not only do patients become incapable of carrying out
their normal tasks but they become housebound and finally
bedridden.   Pressure sores and infection of the bladder
need to be watched for.   The morale of the patient and his
family is under great strain.

The case of Mrs C. (quoted in 'Social Work in Medical
Care' (9)) is a good illustration of both the nature of the condition and the types of help which social work can offer.

Disorders of the brain

Spondylosis in the spine at the level of the neck can compress the vertical artery which runs in a channel within the
vertebral column and supplies the hind brain.   Disturbances
of vision and sometimes of consciousness may result.
'Drop-attacks', wherein old people fall without warning,
are also believed to relate to transient failure of the vertical blood supply to the hind brain.

'Parkinsonism' is an affliction of older people which was
already discussed in Chapter 4.   It is characterised by
rigidity of limbs and a tremor.   The motion of thumb and
forefinger which resembles pin-rolling is typical of this
tremor.   There is also a loss of expression in the face and
a hurried walk with shortened steps.   It is treatable up to
a point.   In mild cases drugs related to belladonna have
long been known to help.   A much more effective recent
treatment is 'Levadopa'.   In resistant cases a surgical
approach is possible by insertion of a long needle into the
appropriate part of the brain substance.

By far the commonest neurological threat to mobility
results from a stroke.   A stroke is a complication of the
degenerative condition of arteries known commonly as
'arteriosclerosis', but technically as 'atherosclerosis'.
Roughening of the inner lining of the arterial tube encourages the blood flowing through it to clot and thus to block

the tube.   This prevents oxygen reaching the part of the
brain which the particular artery supplies, so that the part
loses its function.   When arteriosclerosis is accompanied
by an abnormally high blood pressure, any weakness in the
arterial wall is a possible site for a burst and a haemorrhage.   This also destroys the function of a part of the
brain.   Either of these pathological happenings is most
liable to occur beneath the surface of that part of the brain
which controls the movements of speech, face, arms and
legs (on the opposite side of the body).   In Chapter 3 we
have discussed a case of a stroke in some detail, including
details of its effects, treatment and prognosis.

Disorders of the circulation limiting blood and oxygen supply to the organs of movement

The arteries of the legs are liable to be narrowed by
arteriosclerosis in older people.   A typical pain ensues,
called 'claudication'.   This comes on after walking a certain distance, ceases when the person stops, and comes on
again when he walks the same distance again.   In some
instances surgical grafting of the arteries may be helpful.
Natural improvement does, however, sometimes occur
because other arteries appear to take over some of the functions of the one which is narrowed or blocked.

Disorders of the feet

Surveys of unmet need in old people have consistently
shown that chiropody is needed to deal with painful corns,
callosities and toe-nails.   These minor problems prove to
be very common reasons for limited mobility in the old and
they may lead to more serious problems of immobility as a
result of stiffening of the joints through non-use.   Relief
is easy and highly beneficial.

Phobic states

These cause an unusual type of partial 'immobility'.   There
are many kinds of phobia but among the more common and
important, in their effect on mobility, are a fear of going
out of the house and of open spaces (agoraphobia) and fear

of closed spaces (claustrophobia). These states of
irrational fear are very real to the sufferer, but often very
hard for other people to understand and therefore to sympa-
thise with. Views as to their cause vary, but basically
their nature is not well understood and this makes effective
treatment difficult. A variety of treatments have convin-
cingly claimed successes - psychotherapy, drugs, behaviour
therapy and hypnosis. Social workers can try to minimise
the effects of a given phobia on the life of the patient herself
(women are more prone to both agoraphobia and claustrophobia) and her family, and to provide them with support
while treatment takes place.

LONELINESS

'In the year of Christ 1571 at the age of thirty-eight, on the
last day of February, his birthday, Michael de Montaigne,
long weary of the servitude of the court and of public
employments, while still entire, retired to the bosom of the
learned virgins, where in calm and freedom from all cares
he will spend what little remains of his life, now more than
half run-out.' Montaigne lived alone in his tower, writing
his essays, for most of the next twenty-one years until he
died at the age of 59.
     Some people prefer to live alone. Most of us wish to do
so sometimes. Loneliness is something different. It is
possible to feel lonely in company or in the presence of a
crowd. The word implies a feeling rather than a fact:
suffering, not a preferred choice.
     The capacity to be alone without feeling lonely is directly
related to stages of maturity. According to the late Dr
Winnicott, this capacity: 'is one of the most important signs
of maturity in emotional development'. (10) Being capable
of being alone implies a degree of self-sufficiency and a
resulting sense of security.

The origins of loneliness

According to Reichian psychology, the origins of loneliness
lie in the separation of the newly born infant from his mother
on the severance of the umbilical cord. Whether or not one
subscribes to this particular explanation, it is hard to deny
that much of human experience is characterised by a conflict

between the need to develop and enhance individuality and the need for meaningful sharing with other people. Some of this conflict can be perceived in terms of ambivalence between independence and dependence – the inevitable accompaniment of man's dual nature: personal and social.

When it is thought of in these terms, a degree of loneliness can be accepted as being both a common and a normal ingredient of the human condition. It only becomes problematic for some people in some circumstances. The latter are derived from either the personal characteristics of the individual or the conditions in which he finds himself, or usually a mixture of both.

Loneliness constitutes a burden and a worry to those who, for whatever reasons, lack a sense of personal security and worth and have therefore to rely excessively for 'confirmation' (to use an Existentialist term) by others. For a sense of personal security and worth to exist, the individual must feel valued for who he is, rather than be accepted conditionally on the basis of some tangible achievement. Unfortunately, however, such conditional acceptance is the basis of many relationships in contemporary society and th this in turn calls for a higher degree of personal self-sufficiency than would be required in a more closely knit and supportive society. Those who lack such self-sufficiency and who are therefore particularly vulnerable to loneliness are individuals who have been deprived of adequate love and security during their formative years.

The younger the child, the greater his dependence on others: this is why very young children cannot be left alone. To them, the absence of the mother or mother-substitute for even a very short period represents complete and lasting abandon. Proust described unforgettably the loneliness of a slightly older child in an upstairs room listening to the chatter of the grown-ups in the garden below his window. As children grow up, their conception of time develops and their tolerance of separation also becomes greater, because they can now anticipate and look forward to the absent person's return.

Every stage of life presents its own challenge in terms of managing to be alone and being able to tolerate a degree of loneliness. This was implicit in much of our discussion in Chapter 4, but the importance of the subject justifies a more explicit reference to the relationship between age and loneliness.

The adolescent period makes particularly heavy demands

in this respect. Being a transitional phase between childhood and adulthood, adolescence is typified by a number of
internal conflicts, often very severe. They are all aspects
of the process of establishing a personal identity which
carries with it the dual requirement of separateness from
others and a sense of belonging to society. Attempts to
resolve these conflicts are often accompanied by feelings of
profound loneliness due to inability fully to share intimate
experiences with others. A contemporary French philoso-
pher has in fact suggested that adolescence and illness have
this in common, that they both provide the individual with a
singularly intense experience of loneliness. In adolescents, loneliness can lead either to a withdrawal into themselves and a degree of personal seclusion which at times can
be extreme, or to an active involvement in group activities
of various kinds with his peers. The latter may be either
socially acceptable or result in delinquency: in either case
they usually constitute defensive behaviour against loneliness rather than a genuine gregariousness. Dr Winnicott
called this phenomenon 'the adolescent doldrums'. (11)

Loneliness can also play an important part in the so-
called 'middle-life crisis' in both men and women when they
have to come to terms with the fact that they have either
reached or passed the peak of their achievement in many
social respects and have to rely on their own sense of personal worth and self-respect.

Old age is another crucial period for loneliness. Old
people have to come to terms with themselves to an even
greater degree than people in the younger age groups
because they face approaching death. A realistic facing
up to this task without shirking its many painful aspects
tests what Ericson has called 'ego integrity'. (12)

Loneliness as a problem

Most people at most times are able to manage their loneliness. Doctors and social workers are foremost among
those in the helping professions who encounter people who
have feelings of excessive or overwhelming loneliness.
They have to be ready to offer them help and solace.

Important losses are a common cause, be these losses of
significant people, of cherished possessions, of valued
functions, or of status. Bereavement results in one of the
most acute forms of loss: the widower who discovers on

wakening each morning that his bed is empty; the widow who
waits for her husband to come in from work in the evening
and sets his place at the table.   Such acute distress may
last for weeks, or months, or years.

Severe loneliness may also result from the loss of one's
country and culture, as in the case of refugees or immigrants, or from other forms of radical change in milieu.

Loneliness does not, however, necessarily imply loss:
there are some lonely people who have never felt otherwise.
Some have a lifelong difficulty in giving and receiving affection or making friends.   This may be due to personality, to
being 'shy', because they feel themselves to be different and
are self-conscious as a result.   Such self-consciousness
may result from what are felt to be deficiencies in appearance: the shape of the nose, a loss of hair, the 'wrong'
height or weight.   This sense of difference and the consequent self-imposed social isolation may assume more subtle
forms: the boy who does not like games, the girl who thinks
herself ugly, the adolescent who is aware that he or she is
attracted only to their own sex.

Although, as we have argued, loneliness is a personal and
a subjective experience, nevertheless social factors play an
important part in making some individuals more vulnerable.
The social isolation and resulting loneliness of many retired
people and middle-aged widows (as, for example, documen-
ted by Tunstall (13) and Marris (14) respectively) illustrate
the extent to which many people in our society are dependent
on 'instrumental' types of relationship rather than being
involved in 'expressive' relationships - only these being
capable of allowing for a genuine inter-personal interchange.

In old age, the absence of children and grandchildren
within easy reach can greatly contribute to loneliness,
especially in those who are widowed.   It is, of course, not
just physical proximity which is important: to have children
and grandchildren and to feel neglected by them is more
likely to create loneliness than not having any.

For those who are unmarried loneliness may start when
parents die, and this will be especially true for the unmarried daughter who has devoted herself exclusively to
looking after them.

Serious illness evokes a great sense of loneliness
because basically it is an intensely personal experience
which cannot be shared with others.   It reveals the reality
of man's uniqueness which lies at the root of all loneliness.
The following passage from Solzhenitsyn's 'Cancer Ward'

conveys the awareness of being on one's own in the face of
a grave disease:

The harmonious exemplary Rusanov family, their well
adjusted way of life and their immaculate apartment – in
the space of a few days, all this had been cut off from
him. It was now on the other side of his tumour. They
were alive and would go on living, whatever happened to
their father. However much they might worry, fuss or
weep, the tumour was growing like a wall behind him,
and on his side of it he was left alone.

Illness is in fact one of the commonest reasons for experiencing loneliness for those who normally do not know it.
Break with normal routine, immobilisation, and the reminder
that one is not immortal, constitute a threat for most people.
Those who have sufficient personal resources to cope with
it can benefit by the experience by becoming more mature
and better able to face loneliness in the future. For those,
however, who lack the necessary inner security to bear
with the absence of customary 'props' to living, such as
'keeping busy' to avoid reflection about the meaning of life,
the enforced loneliness of illness may prove too threatening, and, instead of being beneficial, lead to despair or
rebellion.

Loneliness can result in illness as well as be caused by
it. Lonely people tend to consult doctors a great deal;
they may have no one else but doctor or social worker on
whom they can depend for human contact, sympathy and
advice.

However, they rarely come complaining of loneliness.
They may consult frequently for minor complaints or appear
to invent pretexts for their visit. They feature largely
among patients whom doctors resent as 'time wasters'.
Their complaints only make sense if the context of loneliness is understood; whether such understanding leads to
acceptance will still depend on the doctor they meet.

A degree of depression is a common feature in these contacts, though often not openly acknowledged. More usually
it is detected through skilful interviewing on the part of
the doctor or social worker to whom the person comes with
some other problem. Depression is a portmanteau term
for a range of states which will be discussed more fully in
the next section. For the present purposes it is important
to note that severe depression can result in suicide and that
there is also a close association between loneliness and
suicide, as found by Sainsbury, (15) for example. Detec-

tion of depression in lonely patients/clients is therefore of
the utmost importance.

How can lonely people be helped?

Perhaps the most important single element is to reduce
fear through the recognition and acceptance that a degree of
loneliness is normal. This overall approach must be
accompanied by help of a more specific kind, depending on
the extent of the loneliness experienced and its causes.
Loneliness due to some specific factor such as an illness,
bereavement, or retirement, in someone who has not
suffered from it before, is relatively easy to respond to.
An understanding relationship with a doctor or social
worker, providing the lonely person with a positive experience of dependence, will usually enable him to regain his
inner equilibrium after a time, without his becoming chronically dependent on them.
The relationship with a doctor or social worker loneliness is less
specific and is largely due to a defective sense of self-
esteem are much harder to help. Care has to be taken not
to encourage excessive dependence which cannot be adequately met within the context of a professional relationship.
The first essential is to recognise the problem for what
it is, despite its many disguises and despite some people's
reluctance to admit it. For example, a woman of 60, unmarried, living with her only surviving sister, with whom
she could not get on, complained of a succession of physical
disorders, none of which fitted the textbook patterns. Her
colds lasted for weeks, the backache was extreme, though
this was not confirmed by either observation of her behaviour or by X-ray examination. The frequency of micturition of which she complained was never accompanied by
evidence of an infection. Diarrhoea on a couple of occasions caused a panicky telephone consultation. Yet, as
soon as any one of these physical problems was attended to,
the patient seemed to lose interest in it and to move on to
another, ensuring frequent and close contact with the
doctor. When she rang, she expected her voice to be recognised without giving her name. The problem of loneliness, although not expressed directly, could be 'read
between the lines'. It existed despite the proximity of her
sister and what appeared to be a relatively normal past,

when she had good parents, another sister and a brother,
many friends and plenty of money. In her own view, loss
of money had caused the change and served as an explanation why the present was empty, the future looked bleak and
the past the only time worth talking about. In her doctor's
mind several questions remained puzzling: why did this
physically attractive woman never marry?; is it really
largely her sister's fault that they cannot get on with each
other?; why does she so often make him feel angry?

This case illustrates a frequent difficulty for the social
worker or doctor in dealing with lonely people. They are
asked to fill the role of the absent spouse or parent, and
this is manifestly out of the question. The need of these
individuals for a nurturing relationship is often much
greater than any one substitute can possibly supply. Since
the lonely need above all someone upon whom they can rely
to be there and to act consistently, it is vital not to be
seduced by their insatiable needs, but to offer them from
the outset only what can be sustained. It is often best to
explain at an early stage the limits of what can be provided,
whether in emotional support or in practical help.

It may be possible to extend support by calling in a voluntary visitor, or linking the lonely person with an appropriate voluntary organisation, self-help group, evening class
or some other form of contact. It is, however, important
not to underestimate the difficulties experienced by many
severe 'isolates' in managing even such restricted contacts
with other people. A premature forcing of the pace could
have the opposite effect and a vulnerable individual's tenuous sense of self-confidence could become further undermined leading to a further retreat into himself.

An important principle referred to throughout this book
and which needs to be borne in mind when trying to help
lonely people is that human beings need to be able to give
and to be needed, they do not only need to be given to and
valued by others. It is important to try to help the lonely
individual discover what it is he or she has to offer to
others, and then help him find the right opportunity for
making his contribution. Striving for success in establishing (or, more usually, re-establishing) this capacity is
well worth the effort involved because there is no more
satisfactory or radical cure for loneliness than this.

ANXIETY AND DEPRESSION

Feelings of anxiety and depression are experienced by
almost everyone at some time in their lives and they do not
necessarily imply the presence of an emotional disorder or
a state of illness. Indeed their absence in circumstances
which would evoke them in most people, would be surprising and a cause for concern. When then do symptoms of
anxiety and depression cease to be 'normal' and become the
signs of a more serious condition? No one, so far, has
clearly defined this distinction but in practice it is the fact
that a person is complaining of feeling anxious or depressed,
together with the severity of these feelings, which provides
the most reliable guide. Any assessment must above all
take into account the appropriateness of the reaction to the
circumstances described or observed. Failure to complain
of causative factors does not, of course, exclude the possibility of their existence and the need to intervene. Equally, in the case of depression in particular, its presence
may not be openly admitted but may reveal itself in various
indirect ways: in feelings of despondency and in failure to
cope. As has already been stressed in the previous section, a skilled assessment of the nature of the problem is
of the utmost importance, not least because this may occasionally prevent suicide.

Since fear and misery are feelings known to us all, there
is no need to describe at length the difference between
anxiety and depression. Anxiety refers essentially to the
future (although the future may mean the next minute or
hour), whilst depression is more likely to refer to the past
or the present. Anxiety and depression often go together,
but their relative proportions vary. Observation in the
field of general practice suggests that not all anxious
people feel depressed, but that many depressed people
suffer from feelings of anxiety as well. This is an important point to bear in mind, because depression may be concealed behind anxiety and yet may be the symptom which
predominantly needs help.

To discuss fully the innumerable causes of either symptom
is neither possible nor appropriate for present purposes.
One important point, however, is that the predominant
cause or causes may lie either 'inside' or 'outside' the
person. The distinction is clearest when the symptoms
are of recent origin and are very marked. In such a case
one is bound to consider whether a particular event or

person has precipitated the change: an external factor such as bereavement will often be found. Sometimes, however, no such traceable cause can be identified and something appears to have changed inside the sufferer. The clearest example of this is the person who suffers bouts of depression at predictable intervals. These two different forms of depression are sometimes called 'reactive' and 'endogenous' respectively. It is important to note, however, that the distinction refers primarily to the different weighting of the 'inner' and the 'outer' factors in a depression - 'pure' examples of each are uncommon.

Anxiety and depression invariably involve suffering, but there are the widest differences in degree. To experience diarrhoea or the feeling of 'butterflies in the stomach' belongs to normal anxiety as in students before their examinations. But at the other extreme is the state of total apathy and non-functioning of mental and physical processes typical of severe melancholia.

Common indicators of depression are an overall slowing up of thought processes and physical movements, excessive fatigue, constipation, insomnia (early morning waking is particularly typical in cases where depression is accompanied by a high degree of anxiety), loss of appetite (although compulsive overeating is often found in milder cases), loss of sexual desire and potency, and a general loss of interest in and enjoyment of normal activities and contacts with other people.

Undisguised anxiety states show themselves as difficulty in concentration, irritability, tenseness, tiredness and difficulty in getting off to sleep; headache is the commonest physical manifestation.

Doctors and social workers encounter the greatest difficulty in recognising underlying states of anxiety and depression where these are heavily disguised by a variety of physical symptoms or illnesses. These may range from frequent headache, backache or digestive upsets for which no organic cause can be found, to an unusual frequency of virus and other infections. Complaints of this kind can resemble hysterical conversion symptoms, particularly in the case of those patients who cannot tolerate even the slightest suggestion that emotional factors may play a part in their physical complaints. Such people are unusually intolerant of experiencing even small amounts of mental pain and succeed in denying and repressing their emotions to such an extent that all they are left with are physical symptoms and disabilities.

Though they have some common features, patients suffering from conditions which are designated as psychosomatic,
e.g. ulcerative colitis, some forms of asthma, etc., differ
in one very important respect – their physical symptoms
have a definite somatic basis.

There are some people, and social workers and doctors
are particularly likely to meet them, who appear almost
permanently anxious or depressed. Specific causes of
this are very hard to identify: they are both multiple and
relate to the individual's past, often remote, as well as to
his current circumstances. The recent work of Brown and
Harris (16) has been of great value in indicating the kinds
of past experience and present events which produce liability to these symptoms. They have identified a number of
social and psychological factors, but the possibility of some
added influence of physical or hereditary factors must not
be overlooked.

It is not surprising that anxiety and depression occur
frequently when a person is physically ill. Who does not
feel depressed by influenza, especially at the stage of convalescence? Who would not feel anxious in the case of a
heart attack or a stroke? Because of the normality of such
reactions in such circumstances, it is easy to overlook the
reality of the suffering inherent in them. This applies in
particular to doctors, since they have an important and
absorbing technical task in relation to the physical needs of
the case. To the patient, however, his emotional state may
be the more important of the two: failure by those who care
for him to perceive his anxiety or depression and to respond
may be disillusioning and may be felt as rejection or
callousness. The relative importance to people of their
mental and physical suffering is an open question, but those
who have experienced severe degrees of both almost invariably declare that mental suffering is the greater of the two.

Treatment of anxiety and depression

It is usually important to try and bring the problem into the
open. The mere fact of doing so is often helpful as it indicates interest and concern. The task may either be relatively easy where people are very ready to talk and share
(sometimes at the risk of inundating one with a mass of
information) or, it may be extremely difficult and delicate
when the underlying conflicts are deep or too hard for the

patient/client to face. In either case, great sensitivity is
needed in judging what constitutes helpful sharing, in res-
pecting the person's ability and willingness to look at his
problems, and in going at his pace. Some individuals need
a good deal of encouragement before they can begin to
reveal their innermost thoughts and feelings; if it is not
offered, there will be no chance of a solution to their problem, or at least relief, being found. One must not underestimate, however, the difficulties involved in taking such
an active stance: it is in the nature of their problem that
these individuals will resent, initially at least, being asked
to expose their psychological suffering, especially if they
had invested a great deal in disguising it by physical ill
health, financial mismanagement, marital strife, etc.

The process of exploring the symptoms and their causes
is equivalent for the doctor to the process of physical diagnosis, but there is a difference in that the exploration here
can only be carried out by means of a discussion with the
patient. Understanding increases in both parties simultaneously and is accompanied by relief for the patient: thus
diagnosis and treatment proceed simultaneously too. Such
consultation is a form of psychotherapy; the equivalent
approach in social work is dynamic casework.

The effectiveness of psychotherapy in the treatment of
depression and anxiety depends on their nature and severity.
When 'reactive' elements play an important part, a discussion of the problems sometimes accompanied by tangible
intervention in the external circumstances, is likely to be
highly beneficial. If, on the other hand, internal causes
seem to dominate, symptoms are severe and conform to a
pattern (i.e. occur at predictable intervals without any
external cause), resort to physical treatments is indicated.
These can be in the form of pharmacology or occasionally
electro-convulsive therapy (ECT). These treatments offer
sustained relief to three out of four sufferers from the condition. How they work is not well understood but, in addition to their effectiveness in most instances, their great
asset is that they do not create dependence and so can be
easily relinquished when the depression ceases.

The position with regard to the treatment of anxiety is
less clear. The case for using drugs is less cogent and
states of anxiety unrelated to specific external events are
generally more difficult to help. They also carry a greater
risk of dependence than depressive states, dependence on
the person helping being as much of a risk as dependence on
tranquillisers.

Social work has most to offer in cases of 'reactive' depression and anxiety in which help aimed at influencing the environment in combination with supporting the person can be immensely effective.

However, the case of Mrs D. recorded in 'Social Work in Medical Care' (17) (although unusual in the speed and the radical nature of the improvement) provides an illustration of what can be achieved in some instances of anxiety as well as depression.

SUGGESTIONS FOR FURTHER READING

Given the nature of symptoms all of which can be caused by a number of different factors, there is not a great deal of specific reading available. This is particularly true of the more multi-faceted symptoms such as breathlessness and restricted mobility. On these the reader will be best served by literature which refers to the different medical conditions giving rise to them, much of which will be included in any general textbook of medicine.

On pain we recommend J. Merskey and F.G. Spear (1967), 'The Psychological and Psychiatric Aspects of Pain', Tindall & Balliere.

This is a book on which we have drawn extensively in our own discussion of pain.

On loneliness, of the following books, the first two help to put loneliness in the broader context of personal maturation and social living:

A. Storr (1969), 'The Integrity of the Personality', Penguin.

P. Marris (1975), 'Loss and Change', Routledge & Kegan Paul.

R.S. Weiss (ed.) (1973), 'Loneliness: the Experience of Emotional and Social Isolation', Cambridge, Mass.

On anxiety and depression we include under this section two general textbooks on psychiatry and emotional disorders respectively, one specific text on depression and one on anxiety:

B.C. Bosselman (1950), 'Neurosis and Psychosis', Thomas.

A. Clare (1976), 'Psychiatry in Dissent', Tavistock.

J. Dominian (1975), 'Depression', Fontana.

C. Rycroft (1968), 'Anxiety and Neurosis', Penguin.

Chapter 6

Diseases of particular importance

INTRODUCTION

Our selection of diseases for discussion in this chapter has
been influenced by two factors: firstly, by their current
importance in terms of both their prevalence and their personal and social effects; and secondly, by the content of the
other chapters. Many of the conditions referred to in
Chapter 4 because of their significance in relation to age
would have been equally appropriate for inclusion in this
chapter; the same is true of many of the diseases discussed
in Chapters 3 and 5. It has, therefore, been something of
a dilemma to know how to achieve the right balance between
avoiding repetition and not appearing to deny the particular
significance of certain diseases by excluding them from this
chapter.

We have opted for a compromise solution. We have listed
in this chapter certain groups of diseases which, in our
view, meet the criteria of particular importance, as defined
above, with the exception of rheumatic diseases which are
extensively treated in the section on mobility in Chapter 5.
Within these groups, we have restricted a fuller discussion
to those conditions which are either not referred to elsewhere in the book or which are only mentioned in passing.
For the rest, these are either omitted completely (e.g. as
in the case of multiple sclerosis which does not appear under
neurological disorders because it is discussed under mobility in Chapter 5), or we have limited our discussion to
aspects not adequately covered elsewhere (e.g. as in the
case of strokes under cardio-vascular diseases).

CANCER

The dread of cancer

As cancer is prevalent in our society, most social workers, whatever their particular function or the setting from which they operate, will meet people suffering from one or other of the various forms of this disease. They must therefore be prepared to respond to their many needs and difficulties which its presence creates.

One important feature of cancer, common to all its varieties, is the dread which it conveys. The word itself evokes in many people primitive fears of their bodies being eaten into or rotting away. Other words frequently used in the place of 'cancer' by both patients and their doctors – swelling, growth, tumour, sore, ulcer, etc. – serve as a form of denial and as a safeguard against having to face up to the dreaded reality.

Why is there greater need to deny reality in cases of cancer than in most other diseases? Certainly we are ignorant about its origins. Besides the degree of uncertainty about the effectiveness of treatment, ignorance plays an important part in encouraging speculation and various irrational explanations reflecting individual patients' particular fears and fantasies. Thus, it is quite common for those suffering from cancer to see it as a form of punishment which may either be bitterly resented or accompanied by a profound sense of guilt: some patients deal with this by becoming depressed. While feelings of worthlessness may make some prone to take an excessively pessimistic view of their condition and their chances of cure or improvement, others may project such feelings onto others and blame them for their fate. These patients often include in the range of their mistrust those who are trying to help them over their illness: doctors, nurses and social workers. Such suspicion can make it difficult for the patient to co-operate with the treatment recommended.

The threat which many forms of cancer constitute to a person's 'body image' is another reason why it is so dreaded. All people in various degrees have a strong investment in their body and the organs and functions which belong to it. The formation of one's body image is an integral part of personality development and of personal identity, so it is hardly surprising that any major changes in the body's appearance or functions constitutes a threat to most people's sense of self.

Those who do not value much in themselves other than their bodies will be affected particularly strongly, but even people with a more developed sense of inner self-respect are not likely to escape the trauma altogether. Cancer does in fact frequently entail ulceration, various kinds of discharges, and its treatment can result in organ loss and mutilation (e.g. colostomy or mastectomy).

Another potent cause of fear of cancer is its close association with death. In this respect there is a vicious circle not unlike that which prevailed in relation to tuberculosis before the days of chemotherapy. Because of the implication of a death sentence that the term 'cancer' carries, its use is frequently avoided. It tends to be used only when the disease is in its terminal stages or when a person dies from it. This in turn reinforces the view that cancer and death are synonymous, and prevents the recognition that some forms of cancer are far from lethal, e.g. many cancers of the skin, and that many respond well to treatment if they are identified at a sufficiently early stage.

Severe pain is very commonly associated in people's minds with cancer. Different forms of cancer vary greatly in the extent of the pain they cause; some are almost painless. Fear of pain is also increased because people do not realise the recent progress in the provision of drugs which can control pain to a great extent. They are not, however, always used as effectively as they might be and the widespread fear of pain among patients and potential patients continues to have validity.

What is cancer?

Cancer's a funny thing.
Nobody knows what the cause is,
Though some pretend they do;
It's like a hidden assassin
Waiting to strike at you.
Childless women get it,
And men when they retire;
It's as if there had to be some outlet
For their foiled creative fire.
(W.H. Auden)

'Cancer' is a collective term for a large variety of different sorts of tumours which share the quality of being 'malignant new growths'. New cells of a different sort

appear and proliferate in a particular part of the body, such
as the breast, stomach or lung. Whereas normal cells
which make up any bodily organ have a special nature and
serve a special purpose and seem to obey whatever power
makes the body function in a co-ordinated way, cancer cells
behave differently; they are more primitive and more
powerful; they do not make milk like the normal breast
cells, nor mucus, like the cells which line the bronchial
tubes; arising among such normal cells, they proliferate
wildly and replace normal tissues as they expand; they can
replace even bone. If in their expansion they burst
through the walls of a blood-vessel, the bloodstream can
carry them to a remote part of the body where they form
secondary deposits, called metastases. It is these qualities of local destructive spread and wide dissemination
through the bloodstream that justify the description 'malignant new growths'. These dangerous qualities also distinguish cancer from other new growths such as 'fibroids'
in the uterus, which appear and increase in size and may
press on surrounding structures, but do not erode, replace,
or destroy what is next to them, nor spread to other parts
of the body and constitute therefore in contrast 'benign
growths'.

To understand the cause of a disease is an essential first
step if it is to be prevented. Relatively little is known as
yet about the general cause of cancer. As in so much of
medicine, we have some understanding about the cause of
some types of cancer. For instance, we know that both
cigarette smoking and atmospheric pollution play part in
causing cancer of the bronchial tubes and of lung cancer.
But if all women stopped smoking, there is no reason to
suppose that deaths from cancer of the breast would
diminish; of the causes of this sort of cancer we have no
important established knowledge at all, although diet may
play a part.

It seems likely, in the present state of knowledge, not
only that cancer in different organs has different causes,
but that in any one organ there may be several causes which
work together to start the malignant changes described
above.

The network of knowledge which covers the subject of
cancer and its causes is thus still composed much more of
holes than of threads. It provides the means to prevent
only very few types of cancer - that of the lung being most
important. Partial knowledge does, however, make it pos-

sible to treat and control, at least for a time, several other important forms of cancer.   For instance, cancer of the prostate gland in men, if treated with oestrogen, a female glandular extract, does recede, sometimes for many years, but only to recur, resisting treatment in the end.   Perhaps the most important single implication of the existing under- standing of cancer is the importance of removing or des- troying the malignant cells before they have had a chance to enter the bloodstream and form any secondary deposit in other parts of the body.   Hence the importance of early diagnosis and of such screening devices as cervical smears for example.

The manifestations, prevalence and effects of cancer

The manifestations of cancer depend to some extent on the organ in which the new and parasitic cells first arise.   It is usually possible to identify the site of origin.   The com- monest sites of origin are: in the female, the cervix, the uterus, the breast, the large bowel and stomach; in the male, the stomach, the lung, the large bowel, and the pros- tate gland.   However, cancer can occur in almost any part or organ of the body and it can attack every type of tissue.
Cancer of the breast – to take one example – is usually first noticed as a painless hard lump in a part of the body which is normally soft.   The victim feels perfectly well. In an old person such a lump may increase in size only very slowly and spread only locally, but in younger women spread to nearby lymph-glands tends to occur quickly and so also via these glands and the bloodstream to other parts of the body, particularly to bones.   Cancer in bones is usually painful, so that it is ominous when any woman who has had a growth removed from a breast begins to complain of 'rheu- matic pains'.   At this time of spreading growth a sense of illness starts, together with loss of appetite and weight. The course of the disease towards death can be as short as three months, or as long as twenty years.   Can such a fatal outcome be stopped, even if the disease itself cannot be pre- vented?   Surgical removal of the lump originally found can be completely successful.   The outcome appears to depend on whether there has already been a spread outside the area removed at the time of operation.   The passage of time is the only way in which spread or no spread can be revealed, so that no surgeon can be entirely confident at the time of

operation that he has removed the whole danger, although he is often in the position to know how the odds are weighted.

Cancer of the lung may first reveal its presence as a persistent cough or through the coughing of blood, or as a pain in the chest. It may be found by chance as a shadow on an X-ray. It may underlie pneumonia and must always be suspected in anyone past the age of 30 who has a chest infection for the first time, especially if they smoke. Its presence can be proved by finding cancer cells in the sputum coughed up or by performing a bronchoscopy. Whether it can be removed at all will depend on proximity to vital structures near the heart. Whether removal will result in permanent success depends on the extent of spread, as with cancer of the female breast and many other forms of cancer. If it has taken place, the outlook is very poor. Radiotherapy or chemotherapy can sometimes delay the inevitable result, but not in every case.

It must be said that malignant new growths in general are fatal diseases, accounting for the second largest percentage of deaths in the population. But cancers are also very unpredictable in course; the rate of deterioration in victims of the disease even without treatment, does therefore vary very greatly.

In general cancer is not now occurring more frequently except for cancer of the lung, the incidence of which has increased in the last 50 years, coinciding with the increase in cigarette smoking in the population. More recently the increased incidence in women of both lung cancer and smoking has been particularly striking. Prevention, in this instance, encounters the very powerful human urge to seek immediate gratification of a craving without due regard to long-term implications.

The medical and surgical management of cancer

Surgical removal of the primary growth is still the most important defence against this group of fatal diseases. It is usually undertaken where the primary growth is in an accessible part of the body and there is no evidence from tests that spread to another part of the body has already taken place. The absence of evidence of spread is not a proof that this has not already taken place. Patients are almost always given the benefit of the doubt and this explains those sad situations where a successful removal of a

primary growth is carried out, only to be followed soon by
a general deterioration.

The other available treatments are by 'radiotherapy' or
'chemotherapy'. Radiotherapy uses the power of X-rays
to achieve selective destruction of cancer cells. The destructive ray is concentrated at the site of the tumour, but
distributed lightly over normal tissues. If the tumour is
deep in the body, the rays can be directed from a different
angle on different occasions, so that no one area of normal
tissue receives as much radiation as the tumour site. A
few cancers are so sensitive to X-rays that they are destroyed and do not recur (e.g. cancers of the skin). In
most instances, however, the results of radiation are temporary. The treatment is nevertheless of great value in
relieving distressing symptoms and in prolonging life.

Chemotherapy or drug treatment, is more recent. It
has its greatest successes in leukaemia – cancer of the
white cells of the blood – but it is also used in other forms
of cancer with more variable results. There are now a
number of chemical agents capable of destroying cancer
cells, at least temporarily, without the destruction of
normal cells.

The contribution of the social worker to the treatment and
care of cancer victims

Social workers are used to trying to help people express,
share and face up to painful realities of various kinds.
This form of help is founded on the conviction (well valida-
ted from both psychology and practical experience) that the
very fact of acknowledging a situation, instead of running
away from it, makes it less fearsome and more manageable.

The fear of cancer leads some people to ignore certain
signs and symptoms which might be associated with early
cancer, such as internal bleeding or a lump in the breast.
A person who knows that he or she is jeopardising his life
by not seeking medical advice and yet is afraid to have their
dread confirmed if they take it is likely to be in great distress. There is also a serious risk that by the time they
have braced themselves to see a doctor or been forced to do
so by the worsening of their symptoms, their condition may
have reached an untreatable stage.

Social workers have contacts with many people in the
population who may be particularly liable to delay medical

consultation and may have the additional difficulties
resulting from their social position and status to which
reference was made in the earlier chapters. Social
workers therefore have ready means to identify these difficulties and help clients overcome them, so that they can
avail themselves of treatment at a stage when this is most
likely to be effective. The necessary prerequisite for many
people is to have an opportunity to express their fears and,
where these are being denied, to be helped to recognise
them.

Ongoing support, during the period of investigation which
precedes the making of a diagnosis, is of crucial importance. People may need a good deal of encouragement and
comfort whilst having to cope with the investigations, which
may be painful or frightening, and with the period of uncertainty.

If a diagnosis of cancer follows the investigations, the
social worker who has known the patient for some time may
be in a position to help over the difficult issue, frequently
oversimplified, whether or not the patient should be told
'the truth'. As Dr Cecily Saunders, among others, has
demonstrated, (1) truth can mean different things to different
people. The more important and emotive a subject, the
more its discussion is influenced by the complex dynamics
of inter-personal communication.

Some people, and they appear to be in the minority, are
anxious to be told as many facts as possible about their condition, treatment and prognosis; they are able to accept and
act upon this knowledge in ways which enhance their personal autonomy. At the other extreme, there are those who
equally clearly do not want to know any of the painful or
threatening facts about their condition and what is likely to
be its outcome. They have a strong wish to delegate all the
responsibility for treatment and the decisions relating to it
to the doctor who 'knows best'.

The great majority come between these two extremes.
They want to be told the important facts regarding their
health and the future outlook, but they also need these facts
to be presented in a psychologically acceptable way, and
this usually includes an element of hope. It is this which
largely explains why the patient's own perception of his
condition cannot be quite as 'objective' as that of an outsider.

Social workers have been known to adopt a rather naive
and unrealistic attitude in this very complex and difficult

area. Their expectations about what doctors should tell
their patients and what patients can accept from their doctors sometimes suggest that they have forgotten that 'feelings are facts'.

Telling a person his medical diagnosis is clearly a doctor's job. A close collaborative relationship between a
doctor and social worker based on mutual trust and respect
may enable the social worker to play an important role in
acting on the basis of her knowledge of a particular patient
and his needs and providing the doctor with information
which will help him decide what to say and how to convey the
message. The social worker has an even greater contribution to make in helping a person use constructively what he
has been told by clarifying unrealistic ideas, offering psychological support and helping him in various concrete ways
to make constructive use of his knowledge. These include
making communication easier between the patient and various
members of his family. It is well known that family balance
is frequently upset by an event of such magnitude as serious
illness in one of its members. This can both create difficulties and offer opportunities for an improvement in previously strained relationships. In both events the social
worker has an important contribution to make by acting as
a catalyst, safety valve, clarifier and supporter.

As already discussed, treatment for cancer can entail
mutilating surgery or other distressing forms of treatment
such as radiotherapy. More will be said about the impact
of surgery in the section on hospitals in Chapter 8.
Regarding radiotherapy, however, whilsts its impact varies,
most patients find this a distressing form of therapy.
Nausea, loss of appetite, and loss of hair, are the most
common physical side-effects of radiotherapy. At the psychological level many people are affected however by the
impact of the invisible power resting in the X-ray machine.
The fact that they have to be isolated from all direct human
contact during the actual period of irradiation creates a
sense of great loneliness and often fear.

The last stages of illness, in the absence of appropriate
provision and care, can be very distressing and can confirm
all the worst fears with regard to cancer. The part social
workers can play at this point, alongside doctors, nurses,
the family and others, is an important one and will be discussed more fully in Chapter 7.

'Good' social work with cancer patients and their families
is fundamentally the same as 'good' social work with any

other group of clients.   Whilst having to be appropriately informed about the special features of a problem, social workers must always be careful to remember that their distinctive contribution lies in getting beyond this to the person who is experiencing it and whose experiences of it are unique in virtue of his individuality.

The other common feature of all good social work is the ability to maintain the appropriate focus on social functioning and thus to be concerned with both the psychological and the material aspects of human life.   The importance of a sustaining relationship and all this implies in work with cancer patients and their families has been emphasised in this chapter.   What is equally important is the social worker's responsibility to ensure that the sick person has access to all the physical and material comforts which are available to him and which can alleviate his plight and provide him with those pleasures of life which he is capable of enjoying.   Thus additional income during the period of treatment and convalescence can make considerable difference by enabling the patient to have some luxury foods and other commodities which are normally beyond his reach. For example, such voluntary bodies as the National Society for Cancer Relief may provide additional resources of this nature.   Given ingenuity and goodwill, opportunities for acquiring the necessary finance and various services for cancer patients are more readily available than is sometimes recognised.

CARDIO-VASCULAR DISEASES

This cluster of disorders in the cardio-vascular system occurs in the second half of life, and includes coronary heart disease, hypertension, and the effects of hypertension.   They are important as causes of death and disability in the not-so-old and there is already evidence that they may be preventable or treatable.   They are therefore the present focus of particular study and of rapid changes in knowledge and practice.   Valuable active life might be prolonged and premature bereavements prevented, if they could be controlled in the way, for instance, that many infections have been controlled.

Other important cardio-vascular disorders are mentioned only in passing.

The 'cardio-vascular system' consists of the heart and

blood vessels – the pump and the pipes – the anatomy and
physiology of which were described in Chapter 5, in the
section on breathlessness.

Coronary heart disease is part of a disorder which affects
all the blood vessels as well as those of the heart, resulting
from the pathological process 'atherosclerosis'. This
means a change in the nature and appearance of the walls of
the blood vessels; that is, increased rigidity, but above all
irregularity and roughness of the inner lining, which
appears to encourage the formation and deposition of blood-
clots instead of a running stream. The causes of this
change, which can happen in larger blood vessels anywhere
in the body, are very complex and not yet completely understood. Certainly it is more severe in those who smoke
heavily, or are obese. It is increased if the blood pressure is abnormally and persistently high. The fact that it
is not found in certain races and ethnic groups has directed
attention to dietary habits in western cultures, particularly
on the fatty constituents of the vessels' walls and of the
blood itself – notably cholesterol and tirglycerides. But
the understanding of the relation between different diets,
unusual levels of cholesterol and other lipoproteins, and
the experience of cardio-vascular disease in an individual
is still not clear. One cannot yet give indisputable dietary
advice which will prevent further trouble in a sufferer nor,
more important, advocate changes in the diet of a nation
which would reduce dramatically the total incidence of
atherosclerotic disorders, such as heart attacks, angina,
strokes or 'claudicating' pain in the leg.

Hypertension also affects the system as a whole. Pressure raised persistently above normal levels is important
only because of its long-term consequences. It causes
symptoms itself only if the increase of pressure is extreme.
Often it amounts to a chance finding during a physical examination for some other reason because, as already mentioned
in Chapter 4, it is one of the very few things that can 'be
wrong' with a person without discomfort or disability. Its
immediate cause is in the constriction of the small arteries
at the far end of the arterial tree from the heart, but the
reason for this constriction occurring is only partly understood. Persistent raised pressure in the system contri-
butes an important factor of wear and tear which encourages degeneration in blood vessels, including those which
supply the muscle of the heart itself. It also puts a direct
strain on the heart muscle since this has to exert more

force against resistance. Thus, when prolonged, it
endangers the heart, but also several other organs, of
which the brain is most commonly affected – by a stroke –
if an artery either closes or breaks. The subject of
hypertension has become the more important in the last
twenty-five years because relatively easy and successful
control has for the first time become possible.

Coronary heart disease

Coronary thrombosis (alternative terms: coronary occlusion
or coronary infarction) reveals itself as sudden severe pain
centrally in the chest and accompanied by varying degrees
of collapse. It may last for minutes, hours or a few days.
It is, at one extreme, the commonest reason for a person
'dropping dead' or dying in sleep. At the other extreme,
it is a transient episode leading to apparently complete
recovery. Examination at the time will reveal a patient
who is in pain, shocked, apprehensive and possibly breathless. Simple tests will reveal little but a drop in the
normal level of blood pressure. More definite evidence
can be expected from the electrocardiogram and certain
blood tests. Treatment involves control of pain and the
management of consequent disorders of rhythm, or of failure
of the heart as a pump. A coronary thrombosis is always
dangerous and at first unpredictable. Whether all sufferers
should ideally be treated in specially equipped hospital units
is at present a matter of dispute. Such units offer immediate resources for dealing with the unpredictable, which
home care cannot, but their death rate is not less than in
patients nursed at home. In view of the prevailing uncertainty, most doctors would judge it wisest to admit all
except the old, for whom in particular the psychological
disadvantages of acute care units may outweigh the slightly
increased chances of a safe recovery.

Angina pectoris is closely related to coronary thrombosis. The term implies similar central chest pain which
occurs regularly during physical exertion such as walking
a certain distance; it ceases when the exertion stops.
This symptom may be the precursor of a coronary thrombosis, but more commonly it continues for long periods un-
changed. Objective evidence, helpful in distinguishing this
from similar pains, can be obtained from the electrocardiogram (which shows changes in the heart muscle itself

resulting from the impaired or absent blood supply of some
part of it).   A degree of relief is possible by using such
drugs as glyceril trinitrate and 'B-Blockers' like
propranalol.   Surgery – the grafting of a by-pass to the
artery which has failed – is now widely used and successful for severely impaired patients.

Disorders of rhythm, such as the total irregularity called
auricular fibrillation, may be evidence of coronary heart
disease, but any rhythm disorder may arise from other
causes too.   Their importance as immediate consequences
of coronary thrombosis has been mentioned already, but
they can also occur in prolonged form, particularly in older
people.   Auricular fibrillation may be without discomfort
or disability but, if it affects the efficiency of the heart,
it may require treatment.   This is usually by digitalis,
one of the oldest remedies still in use, but highly effective.
Another disorder of rhythm – premature beats – felt typically when a person is at rest, is common, usually unrelated to any pathology and distinct from other disorders of
rhythm.   Those who suffer from this symptom can be un-
equivocally reassured.

Heart failure is experienced by the sufferer as breathlessness, first on exertion, but, if extreme, at rest.   The
immediate cause of breathlessness is the distension of
veins in the lungs and fluid invading lung tissue.   A similar
cause accounts for the other leading symptom of heart failure – swelling of the legs and, if extreme, the abdomen
also.   The symptoms betray a failure of the heart to act as
an efficient pump and the consequent failure of the kidneys
to excrete sodium.   When too much sodium collects in other
tissues of the body, water also collects.   Coronary heart
disease is only one background for this development,
hypertension is another.   In the former condition, the
nutrition of the heart muscle is defective and it may be
scarred and stiffened after the total blockage of one or
more small arteries within its wall.   In the latter, it will
have become unable to compete with additional work and
become inefficient through thickening, stiffening and
stretching.

Heart failure can often be controlled – sometimes for
periods of years.   Digitalis causes a stronger action in the
muscle itself.   Diuretics, by off-loading sodium and water
from the tissues and circulation via the kidneys, relieve
some of the stresses against which the heart has to con-
tend.

Hypertension

Raised blood pressure is a 'physical sign', not a symptom
nor a disease. Its identification depends on examination
with the sphygmomanometer. Readings are routinely made
of the systolic and the diastolic pressures, i.e. the different states of the system when the heart is contracted and
forcing blood out of itself into the arteries; or relaxed and
allowing blood to enter via the veins. Both are important,
but the lower diastolic reading is the more significant.
Both readings vary somewhat from minute to minute, being
influenced both by exertion and emotions. Whether the
level of blood pressure is influenced in the long term by
either factor is still a matter of dispute. It cannot be
assumed that an unusually stressful life automatically
results in a raised pressure.
    The immediate cause of increased pressure is not clear
in the great majority of instances. In a very small
minority of younger patients hypertension is secondary to
other disorders, notably kidney disease. It can also
occur in the final stages of pregnancy, and there is some
association with the use of the contraceptive pill in a small
minority of women.
    Transient elevation of pressure to a high level is part of
normal life. What matters is the effect of persistently
raised pressure over years on the arterial tree, particularly the inner lining of the arteries. As already mentioned, raised pressure encourages atherosclerosis and
this may affect the function and survival of any organ. The
brain is next most commonly at risk after the heart, whether
through the bursting of a blood vessel - cerebral haemorrhage - ot its becoming impenetrable - cerebral 'thrombosis'. Brain tissue supplied by the vessel affected dies and
cannot be replaced as happens in some other tissues. As
already discussed in Chapters 3 and 4, resulting loss of
function depends on the anatomical site of the damage, but
it usually shows itself as loss of power in arm or leg on the
side of the body opposite to the brain damage. Speech may
be affected if damage in a right-handed person occurs on
the left side of the brain, or vice versa. These are the
usual manifestations of 'stroke-illness', but there are
others. Raised blood pressure also tends to affect the
retina of the eye and the kidneys.
    The importance of reducing very high levels of blood
pressure in terms of lowered incidence of complications has

been firmly and repeatedly demonstrated through controlled trials; but the importance of controlling slight persistent elevation is less clear. For some reason hypertension is more dangerous to men than women.

Other disorders of the cardio-vascular system

We have concentrated on coronary heart disease and hypertension. Other important disorders of the cardio-vascular system occur much less frequently. Examples of these are: congenital deformities, particularly of the heart valves; the long-term effects of rheumatic fever on heart valves; the effects of excess or reduction in the activity of the thyroid gland. All these disorders which can influence the efficiency of the heart as a pump and eventually lead to heart failure and death are amenable to some form of treatment, usually with lasting success.

The problem of clot formation and embolism must be discussed a little more fully. It arises most commonly after surgical operations. Inactivity is probably only one factor in causing clots to form in the central veins of a leg, but early mobilisation has secured a great reduction in the incidence of embolism. If a clot does form, it may not remain in situ. If part or all is detached by the stream of blood still flowing, it will jump, pass through the heart and block a branch of the arterial tree supplying the lungs. This event is sudden. If the clot is large, it can be fatal. Lesser clots cause pain, blood-stained cough, illness and some permanent destruction of lung tissue. Embolism can also occur from other causes and in other parts of the cardio-vascular system.

The social work contribution

This has been already extensively discussed in Chapter 3 and in the section on breathlessness in Chapter 5 where discussion has included references to social-work help when younger people are victims of heart disease. What needs adding here is a brief note on social work in the care and rehabilitation of those who have suffered an attack of coronary thrombosis.

The sudden and often unexpected occurrence of such attacks in people who have regarded themselves as healthy, coupled with the very real risk of death, usually has a frightening effect on patients and their families. Although rehabilitation after an attack of coronary thrombosis entails encouragement to resume as active a life as is within the physical capabilities of the individual concerned, no guarantee can be offered against further attacks - on the contrary, vulnerability to future attacks is often greater in those who have already experienced one.

Such a situation of uncertainty is psychologically testing and those who are particularly prone to feeling anxious may succumb to a state of chronic apprehension about their health, leading to an either excessively self-protecting attitude, or reckless behaviour. For this reason, it is very important that as soon as a person recovers from the acute stage of his illness, he is encouraged and helped to make a healthily realistic adaptation to his situation. This will usually entail an appraisal of his life style, followed by some constructive alterations to it. A social worker can play a valuable part in this process by means of both psychological encouragement and support and by any practical steps which may be needed by the patient to help him in the necessary reconstruction of his life.

GASTRO-INTESTINAL DISORDERS

Anatomy and physiology

The gastro-intestinal tract is essentially a long tube. All of it except the mouth, throat and oesophagus or gullet, is contained within the abdominal cavity below the muscular diaphragm. The diaphragm is pierced by a hole which allows the oesophagus above to be joined to the stomach below it. This hole not only allows the passage of food, but also acts as a valve, preventing the strong acid formed in the stomach from rising into the oesophagus.

From the beginning of the stomach to the far end of the tract at the anus the tube measures nearly thirty feet in length. Apart from the stomach itself, which is like a large bag, the next and longest section, the small intestine, forms a complicated series of coils, all tethered to the back wall of the abdomen. This allows a rich supply of blood vessels to reach every coil. The last part - the large intestine or colon - starts at the right hand lower corner of the abdomen, passes upwards to the right hand upper corner and then crosses the top of the abdomen, in close relation to the stomach. From the left upper corner it passes down and backwards to the anus. The penultimate part of it is wider and is called the rectum. It narrows to form the exit or anus, which also acts as a valve preventing faeces from being voided involuntarily.

The whole tube is muscular and capable of squeezing and relaxing, segment by segment in sequence, ensuring the onward passage of whatever is inside it. The contents at the upper end are, of course, liquid or solid foods, the solids changed to some extent by having been chewed in the mouth. From the stomach to the end of the small intestine food is altered by digestion into products which are partly absorbed into the blood stream, which comes in close contact with the crinkled internal surface of the tube; part are left to reach the colon and rectum as waste products. These are voided as faeces.

The abdominal cavity contains other important organs besides the intestinal tract – the liver, gall bladder, pancreas, spleen and appendix. The kidneys lie behind it on each side but are strictly speaking outside the cavity. The main blood vessel, the aorta, supplying blood to the legs and the lower half of the body also lies behind the cavity, but in the middle.

The abdominal 'cavity' is actually filled completely by all these organs, becoming a true space only in abnormal circumstances.

The liver, gall bladder and pancreas are all connected by ducts to the intestinal tract. Through them flow both digestive juices and, in the case of the duct from the liver and gall bladder, certain waste products. The liver resembles a factory which carries out numerous chemical transactions essential to the working of the body. The pancreas, apart from forming digestive juices which act to break down food products, is also an endocrine gland which forms insulin, essential to the metabolism of sugar in the body. The function of the gall bladder, and also of the appendix, remains obscure; both organs seem to be disposable. The spleen serves purposes which relate to the formation and destruction of blood cells; it is therefore in function separate from the gastro-intestinal organs, although contained within the abdominal cavity. It will not be further discussed here.

Disorders

The oesophagus

Difficulty in swallowing is the typical symptom of any disorder here; it is not difficult to distinguish by questioning
that the problem is arising at this site rather than in the
mouth or throat. The difficulty is more likely to be noticed
in swallowing solids and, if it is advanced, food is brought
back by regurgitation. The oesophagus can also give rise
to pain on swallowing or to more continuous pain; this is
felt in the chest or arms or both.
   By far the most important disorder is a cancer arising in
the wall of this tube; it occurs in older people and the
symptoms develop gradually, but inexorably. It is diagnosed by the use of swallowed barium, when narrowing of
the tube is visible to X-rays. It is also accessible to
direct vision through a 'scope'. Treatment is surgical,
and/or by X-rays but the rate of success is low.
   Much more common is the benign, but harmless condition,
hiatus hernia. The 'hernia' means protrusion of a small
part of the upper end of the stomach through the diaphragm
where it is already pierced by the oesophagus. It can
occur whenever there is a reason why the diaphragm and the
hole in it are stretched. It therefore arises in later pregnancy, because of the upward pressure from the abdomen,
now greatly enlarged by the distended uterus. It usually
corrects itself after delivery of the baby. Obesity is the
other common cause.
   The symptoms of hiatus hernia are pain felt at the bottom
of the chest and painful regurgitation of acid-tasting liquid
- 'heart burn'. The reason for the pain is that the hernia
allows the strongly acid liquid in the stomach to rise and
burn the lining of the oesophagus, which is not accustomed,
like its lower neighbour, to this exposure. This is more
likely to occur when lying down, but it does also occur soon
after eating and this makes it difficult to distinguish from
gastric or duodenal ulcer. Weight reduction usually
removes the symptoms.

The stomach and duodenum

Ulceration of the inner lining of the stomach and the first
few inches of the small intestine, known as the duodenum,

is very common. Although isolated attacks occur, it is
typically a recurrent disorder and can occur over most of
a lifetime, particularly in the duodenum. Understanding of
the cause is limited. A specific episode is often associated with eating certain foods – cooked fat being one potential offender. A particular bout of duodenal ulceration
often coincides with a painful emotional experience. But
it would be too simple to say that every duodenal ulcer
always occurs in a particular type of character under conditions of stress.

The typical symptom, whichever the site of ulceration, is
pain felt between half to two hours after eating and, when
present, relieved by eating again or particularly by drinking milk; it is also relieved by swallowing an alkaline
medicine. Vomiting also occurs, especially if the ulcer
causes spasm of the junction between stomach and the duodenum (the pylorus – 'pyloro-spasm'). Diagnosis is unsure
without the use of contrast media X-rays – barium meals.

Attacks typically last from a few days to many months.
There are two important complications – the ulcer may
erode an artery and cause bleeding into the tube, which
shows itself as the vomiting of red blood or a mixture of
blood and acid which appears black, or as the passage of
tarry black faeces. If the bleeding is sudden and extensive, collapse can occur. This usually means admission
to hospital for blood transfusion. The other complication
occurs when the ulcer penetrates the full thickness of the
wall of the tube allowing its contents to seep outside into
the peritoneal cavity. This causes the intense pain and
collapse of peritonitis.

Minor attacks of duodenal and gastric ulceration are
relieved by frequent small meals, and particularly milk.
Antacid medicines give quick but transient relief.

Recurrent and chronic ulceration has, until recently,
required surgical intervention to reduce the acid-creating
capacity of the stomach. The need for operation has been
dramatically reduced in the last five years through the
advent of Cimetidine – a medicine appearing to be more
effective than any other medicinal treatment – or indeed any
operation previously available. Its use may have to be
sustained to prevent recurrence.

Cancer of the stomach

This has to be distinguished from benign gastric ulcer, although in the early stage it may also form an ulcer in the stomach lining. Typically it causes loss of appetite (and later loss of weight), but it may first appear as pain, indistinguishable from ulcer. When suspected, it is essential to use not only contrast X-rays, but also the gastroscope for direct vision, and perhaps the swallowed miniature camera. The only treatment is surgical, but successful removal without recurrence is uncommon.

The small intestine

Apart from duodenal ulceration at the beginning of this part of the tube, disorders are relatively rare in the tube as a whole - the commonest being steatorrhoea (coeliac disease in children) affecting the digestion of fats, and Crohn's disease, a case of which was described in Chapter 3.

The appendix

The veriform appendix is an elongated pocket-like tube attached to the junction of small (ileum) and large intestine (colon). It serves no known purpose in man, but it does sometimes become inflamed and capable of perforation, with seepage of intestinal contents into the abdominal cavity - another common cause of the potentially dangerous condition peritonitis. It is commoner in young people.

Although appendicitis subsides within days, the risk of perforation is high enough for operative removal to be undertaken whenever it is likely that inflammation is present. Doctors seldom forgive themselves for 'missing an appendix' because it may lead to this result.

Typically appendicitis causes an acute episode of pain, starting in the upper abdomen, but settling to the right lower corner, with loss of appetite, fever, vomiting and constipation. Unfortunately the disorder seldom follows the textbook in its behaviour and this is why operation can still result from suspicion rather than certainty about the diagnosis. There are no useful tests beyond the story, questioning and examination with the hand.

The large intestine (colon)

This is the site of a disorder which seems to have become
more common - 'irritable bowel syndrome'. It is also
known as colon spasm, spastic colon or nervous colitis.
It causes intermittent pain in any part of the abdomen,
together with bowel disturbance, either diarrhoea or constipation, and abdominal distension. It is often, though
not always, related to emotional stress and it is not easy to
treat successfully.

It is important to distinguish it from the relatively common
form of cancer which starts in the colon. Hence the use of
contrast medium used as an enema, so that X-rays can
reveal an abnormal segment. Examination also involves the
insertion of a tube - either the older sigmoidoscope or the
more recent colonoscope, which has much more extensive
coverage of the length of the colon.

Surgical treatment of cancer of the colon is relatively
successful, but it may, depending on the site and size of
the growth, entail an artificial opening (stoma) in the abdominal wall, through which faeces are voided into a sealed
bag - 'a colostomy'.

Ulcerative colitis is an uncommon disorder involving part
or all of the colon and causing diarrhoea, bleeding and
prostration. It can be a very severe acute illness in some
instances. Emotional features play a part in its causation,
but once started, a very physical process becomes established. It responds in many cases to enemas of hydrocor-
tisone, but in severe cases may require surgery resulting
in a colostomy.

The anus

Haemorrhoids or 'piles' are a common disorder consisting
of protrusions at the back passage, formed from the skin or
the lining of the last inch of the intestinal tract. These
soft protrusions are filled with dilated veins, resembling
in some ways varicose veins on the legs. Their cause is
still unclear. They occur in people whose bowel habits
seem no different from those of others. They cause bleeding or pain or both. It is usually obvious that the bleeding
comes from near the exit and not from further inside.
Haemorrhoids come and go, but they can be sufficient
nuisance to require usually successful surgical treatment.

Disorders of the liver, gall bladder and pancreas

These organs relate anatomically and in their function to
the intestinal tract, without being a part of it.
   The commonest disorder of the liver is infectious hepatitis. This is a usually mild virus infection, lasting for
weeks and leaving the sufferer somewhat vulnerable for
months afterwards. More rarely it is severe. Starting
like influenza, it does not remit within days, but after about
ten days of headache and nausea, declares itself when the
patient becomes jaundiced. The only treatment is rest.
Infection is at first airborne, but later through the urine
and faeces. A very severe case may require the use of
cortisone.
   Jaundice is caused by a number of disorders, affecting
in various ways the function of the liver. One relatively
common cause is through blockage of the outlet, the common
bile duct. This may be blocked by a stone formed in the
gall bladder, which also drains into the common bile duct;
after escaping from the gall bladder, the stone lodges where
the common bile duct narrows.
   Some stones are opaque to simple X-rays, and require a
special contrast medium to be injected into the bloodstream
to reach the gall bladder in concentrated form. Any stone
lodged in the common bile duct has to be removed for
obvious reasons. It is usual to anticipate the possibility
by removing any gall bladder which contains stones. The
bile duct can also be blocked by a growth forming immediately next to it. One site is in the part of the pancreas
nearest the intestine (the duct of the pancreas drains into
the duodenum at the same point as the common bile duct).
   The liver itself is a very common site for cancerous
growths, but in this country they seldom start there.
Secondary growths in the liver are usually multiple and all
forms of treatment are unsuccessful. This development is
usually terminal, but it does not cause pain. Cirrhosis of
the liver is the name given to a slow degenerative disorder
in which the organ becomes hard and finally shrunken, and
which gradually impairs its vital functions. This disorder
has a number of causes, but much the most frequent is
alcohol used in quantity over a long period of time. As the
liver has large reserves of functional tissue compared to
the requirements of the rest of the body, the early stages
of cirrhosis are compatible with reasonable health if
alcohol is totally and permanently withdrawn. The overall

capacity of the liver to carry out its biochemical functions is easily checked by blood tests.

In conclusion it can be seen from the above descriptions that the common abdominal symptoms of pain, vomiting and bowel disturbance are not easily attributable to a particular organ or a particular cause. Similar symptoms can also arise from certain diseases of the heart and lungs, of the kidneys, uterus and ovaries. In addition pain is frequently referred to the front of the abdomen from disorders in the spinal column and the back.

The social work contribution

As will have been gathered, the range and prevalence of various gastro-intestinal disorders means that social workers in all settings are bound to encounter some clients who suffer from some forms of them. Features of gastro-intestinal disorders of particular significance for social work are their debilitating nature and the close relation between some of them and emotional states.

The former characteristic means that where a disorder involving constant pain or discomfort, such as peptic ulcer or severe haemorrhoids, accompanies an already stressful life situation, be it unemployment, poor housing, shortage of money, or conflict with the law, that client's capacity to deal with his problems will be additionally impaired. The latter can easily prove to be 'the last straw' and can turn a precarious state into a disaster. A social worker's appreciation of the importance of that 'trigger' cannot but influence the appropriateness of what he does to help the client.

The effects of psychological stress on the functioning of the gastro-intestinal system are widely recognised in both common experience and professional knowledge, including knowledge in the realm of psychosomatic medicine. An example of the contribution of the latter is the empirical study which was conducted under the auspices of the Medical Research Council by Goldberg (2) and which has shown an important correlation between family relationships and the incidence of duodenal ulcers in a group of young men.

Although such clear relationships between psychological features and gastro-intestinal pathology are not commonly found, the influence of emotional factors as both cause and effect is often considerable. It is important to emphasise, however, that the significance of these factors is not con-

fined to specific 'psychosomatic' diseases. Even on a
purely common-sense basis it is possible to appreciate
that, as the gastro-intestinal system is concerned with the
vital functions of food intake, digestion and absorption, it
is invested with considerable importance for the organism;
consequently any major disturbance in the normal functioning of that system presents a very real threat to well-being
and its very existence. Additional understanding derived
from dynamic psychology points to the symbolic meanings of
food intake and elimination of waste products as well as
indicating the complex ways in which feelings about these
biologidal functions in some individuals may influence attitudes towards significant people in their life. This under-
lines further the importance of the system.

Rather than attempting a discussion of the specific functions of social workers in relation to clients suffering from
particular forms of gastro-intestinal disorder, we should
like to put the emphasis once again here on the importance
of social workers' 'diagnostic sensitivity' to the many
aspects of the bio-psycho-social interaction in these cases.

METABOLIC DISORDERS

Diabetes mellitus

'Sweetness running through' by derivation, this term
refers to a group of disorders which share the common
feature that the blood glucose level is higher than normal.
These disorders are distinct from diabetes insipidus, in
which no sugar is passed in the urine, although thirst and
frequency of urination are striking, as they are in the
youthful form of diabetes.

The two most important forms of diabetes mellitus are
insulin-dependent and non-insulin-dependent. The first is
most frequent in children, adolescents and young adults;
the second in older people, the incidence increasing with
age. The second is far more common than the first, more
difficult to recognise because of its insidious onset and
variable features, but usually less stormy in its course.

Insulin-dependent diabetes is signalled by thirst, frequency of passing water, loss of weight and malaise. The
onset can be rapid over days or weeks and may even present itself with a diabetic coma. This condition can be
mortal and requires urgent and skilled treatment in hospital.

It has to be distinguished from loss of consciousness due to too low a blood sugar.

Untreated insulin-dependent diabetes was always fatal before the discovery of insulin. Insulin is still the main form of treatment; it has to be injected. Diabetics, even children, usually carry this out themselves. But dietary control of carbohydrate intake is also needed. These measures are not only life-saving; their proper maintenance postpones or prevents the very important complications – in the retina of the eye (the threat being blindness), in the kidneys (kidney failure), arteries (particularly of the heart, see section on coronary artery disease) and in the feet (causing gangrene, if severe). Whether or not these occur has long been thought to depend on the maintenance of a normal or near normal blood glucose level. Nevertheless the cause of insulin-dependent diabetes is basically unknown.

Non-insulin-diabetes may present with similar symptoms but it is rather more likely to be found simply on routine urine testing, and to have no symptoms, except perhaps loss of energy, only realised when treatment restores the patient to normal. There is an association with obesity and the possible complications are the same as those of insulin-dependent diabetes. There is, however, every degree of severity, from an obvious case with high blood glucose and many symptoms to a patient without symptoms who passes sugar in the urine, but shows only a small variation above normal in the blood glucose.

The latter may need observation rather than treatment. Most patients with non-insulin-dependent diabetes need to control their intake of carbohydrate. A few need insulin. Antidiabetic agents may be given by mouth, if diet does not control the condition. The sulphonylurea group acts mainly by stimulating insulin release. The best known is tolbutamide.

Insulin, which is usually given more than once a day, can be responsbile for loss of consciousness if the dose is too high or the patient has starved – the blood sugar dropping in either case to levels well below normal. Thus too high a blood sugar and too low a blood sugar can both cause loss of consciousness, but there are usually recognisable distinguishing features. When in doubt, it is safe to assume and treat for insulin coma (hyoglycaemia), but it is possible today to test the level of glucose in the blood by pricking the finger and using a coloured paper which indicates immediately, by the intensity of colour change, the rough level of blood glucose.

Arterial disorders occur more quickly and frequently in the presence of diabetes – whether in the heart, the brain, the retina, the kidneys or the legs. It is generally believed that they can be held off by careful treatment of diabetes, but control being always incomplete, this has not been proved. The same applies to other long-term complications such as cataract, or paralysis in peripheral nerves.

Most social workers are likely to meet some diabetes in the course of their work. How far intervention more specifically geared to the requirements of this disease, such as assisting clients to adhere to their diet and be regular in the administration of insulin, may be needed will depend not only on the nature of the problem but also on both the setting and the nature of the relationship with the client.

Thyroid disorders

The thyroid gland is situated in front of the neck. A swollen thyroid gland has long been known as 'a goitre'. This may or may not be associated with increased or reduced activity of the gland.

An over-active thyroid gland causes increased appetite with loss of weight, a fine tremor of the limbs, sweating, palpitations and breathlessness. Obvious protrusion of the eyes is sometimes a feature. It can be a very serious illness. The cause is unknown, apart from the fact that its onset may be related in time to some personal crisis. The level of circulating thyroxine in the blood is usually sufficient diagnostic proof that the condition relates to the thyroid gland. Without that test, and others more complicated, it is often difficult to distinguish thyrotoxicosis from an anxiety state. Treatment can be surgical, or by the use of radioactive iodine, or by such drugs as carbimazole.

Reduced function of the gland causes the condition known in adults as myxoedema and in children as cretinism. Typically the voice becomes hoarse, the facial features coarse; there is loss of hair, thickening of the skin, increased weight and a feeling of coldness, with mental sluggishness. It is relatively common at or after the menopause in women, but seldom in the gross form here described. The serum thyroxine level is again the basic test. Treatment with thyroxine, given by mouth, is very successful, provided that the disorder has not been very long established, when brain function may have been permanently

impaired.   This condition is occasionally responsible for
a depressive state.

A swollen thyroid gland may be unassociated with either
of these general disturbances, but can cause harm by local
pressure on the windpipe below the larynx.   It can also be
the site of a cancer, which usually appears as a hard lump
on one side.   This has to be removed by surgery.

Obesity

This very common disorder is little understood, despite
very great efforts to study its cause.   It is not easy to
correct permanently, but it is possible if the sufferer is
really willing to make the sustained effort required and
receives encouragement and help.   Increased weight has
long been known to be associated with reduced expectation
of life and it is also associated with certain common cardio-
vascular disorders - atherosclerosis and its effects, hypertension and its effects, diabetes mellitus and diseases of
the gall bladder.   Hence its long-term importance.

It is mysterious that some people can eat any amount of
food without weight gain and others eat little, yet become
obese.   There are well-recorded examples of a sudden
change to obesity being related in time to psychological
trauma in childhood, but this sort of explanation is only
rarely to be found.

The only effective management is dietary.   There are a
great variety of diets which all seem to work, even though
they are based on contradictory principles.   A total quantity of calories is one common factor in most diets; this
has to be reduced.   Physical exercise, if more than half
an hour daily, can play a contributory part in weight
reduction.   Appetite suppressants can help some patients,
but none is totally free from addiction if given to young
people.   They should never be given for long periods of
time to anyone.   By far the most important factor in
deciding success or failure in weight reduction is motivation, but the shared experience, encouragement and penal-
ties involved in such group approaches as 'Weight Watchers'
are of great value also.

NEUROLOGICAL DISORDERS

The term 'neurology' implies the understanding of the physical nervous system and its disorders. The nervous system
consists of the brain, spinal cord and peripheral nerves.
The fact that in some other countries 'neuropsychiatry'
forms a single special branch of medicine emphasises the
difficulty of separating consideration of the brain from that
of the mind - thinking, feeling and behaviour. At the other
extreme, it is difficult to separate consideration of the
peripheral nerves from that of the organs with which they
link - in particular, the muscles, the skin and the organs
of sight, hearing and smell. Indeed the nervous system
must be seen as the most important physical link relating
all the organs of the body to each other and to the mind of
the individual person - the chief agent of bodily awareness
and bodily control.
    Like other systems of the body, the nervous system is
liable to failure of development (as in the condition spina
bifida), to injury (as in fracture of the skull or haemorrhage
from stroke), to infections (like meningitis), to new growths
(as in the cerebral tumour 'glyoma'), and to degeneration
(as in 'Parkinsonism'). When the brain or spinal cord
suffer injury or disease, repair of damaged tissue does not
occur. If there is a degree of recovery, it is due to the
action of nerve cells and nerve fibres other than those
damaged. The peripheral nerves, in contrast, are capable
of self-repair after damage.
    Like other organs, the nervous system undergoes tran-
sient disorders as well as those leaving permanent scars
and disability. In either case the wide range of symptoms
is explicable by the very wide range of anatomical connections and physiological functions - loss of consciousness,
convulsions, vertigo, disturbance of speech, of vision,
hearing and smell, pain in the head or in any part of the
body, loss of power or control or sensation in any part of
the body, including micturition and bowel-function. The
relationship of the brain to mental handicap and mental illness is clear in only certain respects and certain instances
- hydrocephalus, neuro-syphilis and cerebral atrophy are
obvious examples, but they occur very rarely. There is
tantalising, but only suggestive, evidence of biochemical
changes in the brain in such common disturbance of function
as depressive illness.
    The common neurological symptoms and disorders are

headache, fits, vertigo, loss of consciousness, due to a
variety of causes, strokes, multiple sclerosis, spondylosis at various levels of the vertebral column, carpal tunnel
syndrome.

The neurological disorders affecting mobility have been
discussed in the chapter on symptoms. Peripheral neuritis, carpal tunnel syndrome, poliomyelitis and spondylosis
were mentioned briefly as disorders affecting peripheral
nerves; multiple sclerosis as the most important disorder
affecting the spinal cord; Parkinsonism and stroke illness
as disorders affecting the brain.

The symptoms and disorders to be described below have
not been discussed in any other section of this book.

Headache

'Tension headache'

Headache is one of the commonest physical manifestations
of anxiety. Patients describe it in a number of ways,
typically with elaborate similes and an insistence on how
bad it is. Other evidence of anxiety is easily found,
whether by the presence of other symptoms or the manner
in which the patient behaves in the consulting room. The
common description 'like a weight on top of the head' may
indicate a depressive element.

Management is ideally by finding the reasons for anxiety
and helping the patient to remove or diminish them. This
may not be possible. Moreover some people seem to be
very frequently or permanently over-anxious in the face of
problems which do not trouble most of their fellows in any
comparable way. As a means of relief both painkillers and
tranquillisers have a place, but dependence on either is
easy to induce - particularly on tranquillisers; they may
act as an easy substitute for solving a problem which the
anxiety might otherwise drive the person to solve himself.

Headache due to disorders of the neck

An injury to a neck joint can produce pain in front of the
head, because the nerves emerging beside the joints
between the highest vertebrae are distributed over the top
of the skull. The pain may be one-sided or central. Such

pain is, in fact, more often associated with spondylosis of
the same joints and can be relieved by treating this –
whether by rest (the use of a collar), anti-inflammatory
drugs like Phenylbutazone, or by manipulation.

Migraine

This remarkable disorder runs in families, but its cause is
otherwise obscure. Typically it consists of headaches on
one side of the head, associated with transient visual disturbance and nausea, occurring at intervals of weeks, lasting about a day. It may start to occur at puberty and continue for decades at irregular intervals. The sufferer
usually prefers to lie down in a dark room. For the
minority who discover that the headache is brought on by
particular foods, like chocolate, a degree of prevention is
possible. Some are convinced of an association with
accumulated nervous stress – a build-up of stressful circumstances may 'explode' into a migraine attack. Eye disorders, once thought to be important, do not seem to be so.
Partial relief of migraine is obtained by the use of Ergo-
tamine tartrate, but this remedy does not work in every
case. If attacks are sufficiently frequent to merit continuous treatment, Clonodine hydrochloride does seem to help
prevent frequent attacks. However, since most sufferers
have intervals of weeks between attacks, this measure is
less useful than it might seem at first sight.

Loss of consciousness

Loss of consciousness may be transient – lasting seconds or
minutes: or prolonged, lasting hours, days or weeks. The
distinction is important because the types of disorder involved are not the same in the two cases.

Transient loss of consciousness may or may not be
accompanied by convulsions – a distinction best described
as 'faints and fits'. Fits will be the subject of the next
section.

Faints are common, but are of much less importance in
the context of social work than either fits or prolonged loss
of consciousness ('coma'). The commonest causes of faint-
ing ('syncope') are prolonged standing (for instance, when
a soldier has to stand to attention on a hot day) or sudden

emotional stress.   Some people tend to faint, while others never have the experience in a lifetime.   A minority faint with repeated coughing.   Repeated faints in older people may betray an insufficient blood supply to the brain, due to narrowing of the vertebral arteries.   Transient unconsciousness due to drugs which lower blood pressure is now a cause which needs to be remembered.

In almost every instance the emergency management is to see that the patient is horizontal, if he or she has not already arrived in that position! The object is to ensure that the blood supply to the brain is restored as rapidly as possible, something which might not happen if a person is allowed to remain propped up in a chair.

The causes of coma are much more important.   They may stem from disorders within the skull or from general disorders of metabolism.   Examples of the first are haemorrhage from a stroke or from a blow on the head, sudden cerebral infarction from a stroke, or more rarely cerebral tumours.   In all these instances there is a localised mass developing within the skull and, as this will usually be on one side, physical signs will show themselves in the limbs on the opposite side, if the patient is examined.   But diffuse disorders also occur within the skull and cause unconsciousness.   Concussion is a common example: meningitis with or without involvement of the brain itself, less common.

The most important 'metabolic' cause of unconsciousness is poisoning, whether due to alcohol or other narcotics: the occurrence may be accidental or intentional.   The duration of unconsciousness and the chance of full or partial recovery will depend on the drug taken and on the dose ingested.   Other important metabolic causes are diabetes mellitus, in which either a low or a high blood sugar may result in coma: and kidney failure, due to the fact that waste products are not being eliminated.

Coma is a reason for hospital admission, unless a low blood sugar can be both diagnosed and treated rapidly at home.   While it lasts, it is essentially a problem for doctors and nurses, but a social worker may hold vital information if he or she has seen the patient in the past – whether about past physical disorder or past psychiatric problems which might suggest the possibility of overdose of drugs. Another issue with which a social worker already knowing the patient might help is when there has been a noticeable change of personality – as occurs, for instance, when a cerebral tumour is developing.

But the chief role of the social worker is during the period of rehabilitation. What needs to be done will be much influenced by the particular disorder causing coma. The problems with a stroke patient in the stage of recovery are very different from those of someone who has taken an overdose.

Convulsions

Convulsions are usually, but not always, associated with loss of consciousness. Typically the sufferer from epilepsy has a brief warning that it is about to occur – the 'aura' – and then loses consciousness. While unconscious, all muscles at first go into a prolonged spasm, including those of breathing. The face goes blue. Spasm of the jaw causing biting of the tongue and at the same time urine is voided. Convulsions then ensue, usually involving all four limbs. Consciousness is regained gradually, usually within a few minutes, but confusion may be present for an hour or so. A second or third fit may follow quickly, but usually the event is single.

This description is of a major fit – 'grand mal'. But a minor variety, lasting seconds only, also occurs – 'petit mal' – causing a momentary clouding of consciousness and lapse in speech or movement, together with twitching of one or more limbs.

Another variety, named after the neurologist Hughlings Jackson, excites convulsions on one side of the body only and may be unaccompanied by loss of consciousness.

Finally, temporal lobe epilepsy is characterised by a transient impairment of consciousness with confused speech, but preceded by a feeling of strangeness or fear or hallucination, usually of an unpleasant smell. The actual symptoms vary very much from individual to individual.

Fits occur most commonly in childhood. If a fit is associated in early childhood with the onset of a feverish illness, it can be ignored: concern should concentrate on explanation to anxious relatives of its harmlessness.

A single fit may occur in the absence of fever. This is more worrying, but it is not until two or more fits occur that the possibility of an ongoing problem needs to be considered, or preventive treatment started. The labelling of anyone as 'epileptic' has serious consequences for employment and the driving of motor vehicles. Personal relation-

ships can also be adversely affected as a result of the
stigma associated with the term. When repeated fits occur,
or when a single fit occurs for the first time in adult life,
it is necessary to investigate to find any associated disorder
which is likely to be the cause - such as a history of recent
head injury, an infection of the brain, a cerebral tumour or
a degenerative condition of the brain. Even if this involved
no change in treatment, it may help both doctor, patient and
relatives to know the future more accurately.

In general the medical treatment of epilepsy aims to
obtain total prevention of the occurrence of fits by an anti-
convulsant drug. The dose can now be monitored by esti-
mating the level of the drug in the blood, but all anti-con-
vulsants have unpleasant side-effects if the dose is raised
- particularly sleepiness. The side-effects frequently
prevent use of a dose which completely controls the fits.

In this country, the Road Traffic Act specifies that a
driving license may be granted to a person who has suffered
or who is suffering from epilepsy if he has been free from
any attacks, whilst awake, for at least three years. This
concession to those who have attacks when asleep does not
apply to the provision of a license for heavy goods vehicles;
this is forbidden to anyone who has had a fit after the age
of 3.

Adults with epilepsy can do almost any job, except one in
which falling or loss of consciousness might be dangerous
to themselves or others.

Children with epilepsy must not swim unless accompanied
nor should they climb ropes in a gymnasium. It is doubtful whether they should bicycle on a road, but in general
restrictions should be as few as possible.

Prospective parents with epilepsy have a 3 per cent
chance, if one only is an epileptic, of producing an epileptic child: it is much higher if both parents suffer.

Social workers have a potentially important role in helping people with epilepsy to lead as normal lives as possible.
Such a role usually includes an educational component in
relation to the family and others, because of the extent of
ignorance and prejudice which still surround 'epileptic'
fits and those who suffer from them.

Vertigo

This term means a sensation of rotary giddiness, in the
sense that either the sufferer or his surroundings seem to
go round and round: when severe it is accompanied by
nausea, as in seasickness (which is the commonest experience of the disorder). Less typically, the term implies the
sensation of swaying from side to side or up and down, without any rotation.

Patients with vertigo say 'giddiness'. But this word is
also used more loosely - in the sense of 'lightheadedness',
'muzziness' or 'difficulty in thinking' or 'unsteadiness', in
almost any sense of that word.

True vertigo implies a disturbance of the balancing appar-
atus - the semicircular canals in the inner ear or their
connections with the lower end of the brain. It is usually
transient, but the duration depends on the cause.

'Positional' vertigo only occurs when the head is in certain positions - for example, an orchestral conductor regularly experienced it for months if he lay in bed turned on
his right side - but fortunately never when upright. It
recovers spontaneously.

'Vestibular neuronitis' is the commonest explanation for
a sudden illness with vertigo and vomiting. This also
recovers spontaneously, after days or weeks.

Menière's disease is a rarer disorder, occurring in
older people, where attacks of vertigo are always accompanied by increasing deafness and often a persistent noise
- 'tinnitus'.

For the social worker it can be important to be clear
about the nature of vertigo, especially the distinction from
faints and fits (vertigo is only rarely accompanied by
impaired consciousness in any of the conditions described
above). But social problems are only likely to arise if
the symptom is recurrent, or unusually long: or associated
with severe deafness in Menière's disease.

SUGGESTIONS FOR FURTHER READING

We are limiting these to a few key texts in the main areas of
medical practice. For a more detailed treatment of the
less common conditions, the interested reader is advised
to turn to specialist literature.

S. Davidson (1981), 'Principles and Practice of Medicine', 13th edition, Churchill Livingstone.

J. Kyle (1977), 'Pye's Surgical Handicraft', 20th edition, John Wright.

S. Clayton and J.R. Newton (1979), 'A Pocket Gynaecology', Churchill Livingstone.

S. Clayton and J.R. Newton (1979), 'A Pocket Obstetrics', Churchill Livingstone.

C.J.E. Monk (1980), 'Orthopaedics for Undergraduates', 2nd edition, Oxford University Press.

H. Merskey (1980), 'Psychiatric Illness', 3rd edition, Balliere & Tindall.

Chapter 7

The management of chronic sickness and disability and of terminal illness

INTRODUCTION

So far in our discussion of health problems we have mostly focused on disease and have made little mention of its out-come, whether in chronic sickness or disability or in terminal illness; nor did we discuss the particular challenge presented by these conditions. We are, therefore, devoting this chapter specifically to them.

Of the three conditions, chronic sickness and disability have much in common, though the former is more likely to be progressive, resulting in gradual deterioration and ulti-mately death, whilst the latter is often relatively static and any changes are more likely to be the result of the normal ageing process than of pathological deterioration as such. Our discussion in Chapter 5 of multiple sclerosis and osteo-arthritis was concerned with two conditions which differ in this way. However, it is important to stress the relative nature of such a distinction. Perhaps it is more accurate to say that, whilst most chronic sickness also entails a degree of disability, by no means all disability either results from or manifests itself as sickness.

One way of attempting the difficult task of defining termi-nal illness is to compare and contrast it with chronic sick-ness. Both are incurable: chronic sickness, as already suggested, is likely to end in death after a certain period of time; but the label 'terminal' suggests that death is expected to occur in the near or calculable future.

The causes of chronic sickness, disability and terminal illness are multiple. What all three have in common and what has prompted us to devote a separate chapter to them is the foremost importance of proper management aimed at

169

minimising pain, discomfort and distress, and at maximising
the quality of life of those affected by them.

CHRONIC SICKNESS AND DISABILITY

Disability and handicap

In Chapter 4 we referred to the definition of handicap by the
Committee on Child Health Services (1). Here we shall be
mostly concerned with handicap in adulthood but before this
can be properly discussed the difference between disability
and handicap needs to be clarified as the two terms are som
sometimes used interchangeably.

The term 'disability' refers to the existence of an organic
or physiological abnormality, such as the absence, defor-
mity or paralysis of a limb, or deficiency or damage to
organs, including the brain and sensory organs. The same
type and degree of disability may, however, have very different effects on different individuals, depending on their
circumstances. It is these idiosyncratic aspects of disability which are called 'handicap'.

The British Association of Social Workers 'Guidelines on
Social Work with Disabled People' (2) refer to six types of
handicapping factors: environmental (e.g. housing, trans-
port, access to public buildings); societal (e.g. attitudes
within society towards a given disability); availability of
resources (e.g. financial aids to living, various support
services); personality; family relationships; life style
(e.g. loss of a finger will be more handicapping to a violin-
ist than to a singer, and an amputation of a leg to a labourer
than an office worker).

Range and prevalence of disability

Estimates of disabled people in Britain vary from 3 to $4\frac{1}{2}$
million depending on the rigour of the criteria adopted.
We have already referred in Chapter 4 to the fact that
many disabilities result from birth defects. The three
most disabling conditions in children are considered to be
spina bifida (faulty development of the spinal cord), cerebral palsy (damage to the central nervous system) and
muscular dystrophy (a genetic disorder). Many of the
causes of disablement in childhood, youth, adulthood and old

age have been referred to in Chapters 4, 5 and 6: these
include accidents at home, at work and on the roads,
chronic bronchitis, heart disease, strokes, arthritis,
Parkinson's disease and chronic intestinal disorders.
There is also an increasing number of adults who, due to
recent developments in medicine, have survived various
congenital disorders which were formerly lethal either at
birth or in early childhood, e.g. spina bifida and Down's
syndrome.

A further group of disabilities are those derived from
disorders of the sensory organs, especially blindness and
deafness. There are other conditions which, although not
common, cause disruption and unhappiness in the lives of
those who suffer from them, e.g. chronic skin conditions,
kidney disease requiring constant dependence on an artificial kidney machine, certain gastro-intestinal conditions.

A necessary prerequisite to understanding the handicapping effects of a disability is awareness of the major characteristics and variables of the disability itself. The British
Association of Social Workers 'Guidelines' list these as
follows: pattern of onset (i.e. whether a disability is congenital, traumatic, subject to rapid deterioration, or
whether it is insidious); prognosis (i.e. whether the disability is likely to remain static, subject only to normal
developmental changes, or whether it will progress
rapidly); the age of onset (the nature of the crisis caused
by the onset of a disability is greatly affected by the stage
of development reached by the individual, e.g. a disability
restricting movement is particularly damaging in childhood
and early adulthood); systems of the body affected (this
calls for a sound basic knowledge of anatomy and physiology); visibility (some disabilities are very obvious, like
being confined to a wheelchair, whilst others, e.g. a
colostomy, are hidden. Both visible and concealed disabilities present their own distinctive problems, especially
with regard to the disabled person's encounters and transactions with others).

Attitudes in society towards disablement and the disabled

Attitudes towards the disabled members of a society are a
good test of the extent to which people are recognised as
being endowed with inherent value which transcends the
shape, appearance and functioning of their bodies. Atti-

tudes have varied considerably over time in different cultures in relation to both disablement generally and to specific disabilities. Epilepsy provides a good illustration; it was considered 'a sacred disease' in ancient times and those who had it were treated with awe and respect. Today, it is near the bottom of the 'social hierarchy' of disabilities, only spasticity and mental disability being placed below it.

Ambivalence is a characteristic attitude towards the disabled. On its positive side there is the recognition of shared humanity with its accompanying attitude of compassion and desire to be helpful. Paradoxically, however, it is this awareness of a common belonging and destiny which may also result in rejection and insensitivity, if not outright cruelty. Thus, avoidance of contact with disabled people, whether at a physical or a psychological level, can be prompted both by fear and by denial of the fact that none of us is immune from a similar predicament. 'Healthy' people may resent the disabled for being a constant reminder of the tenuous nature of 'normality'. Guilt is another common reaction in dealings with the disabled. People wonder why they themselves have been spared and may defend themselves by deciding that the disabled person must be in some way to blame. Such a rationalisation results in distancing from him as someone who is not one's equal; a connection is thus established between physical infirmity and moral imperfectness. Pitying and patronising behaviour usually accompanies such an attitude; this is the opposite of true compassion, which is based on an acceptance of equality.

The concept of stigma ('spoilt identity') as espoused by Goffman (3) is helpful in understanding the complex dynamics which operate so frequently in the relations between disabled persons and the rest of society. Another useful concept in approaching the problems of disability is that of body image. Schilder (4) has emphasised that 'body image' refers to a predominantly subjective phenomenon, i.e. it is 'that picture or schema of our own body which we form in our minds as a tridemensional unity involving inter-personal, environmental and temporal factors.' Body image thus incorporates cognitive, affective and cultural components. The concept helps to clarify the nature of our investment in our bodies by demonstrating that it extends beyond their purely instrumental value and includes a number of symbolic and mythical meanings. We made a brief reference to this in Chapter 5 in relation to how the heart is perceived.

A significant change to their body is experienced by most
people as a major threat to their personal identity and
integrity. Three different kinds of distorted reaction to
the body have been noted by psychologists. One of these
represents an excessive investment in the body, resulting
in a constant preoccupation with its appearance and functioning. Such practices as unnecessary slimming or undertaking painful and costly plastic surgery for minor or imaginary defects are examples of this attitude. An excessively
anxious stance, reflecting a lack of confidence in the body
and its ability to function adequately, is another type of
reaction. It leads to exaggerated fear about health and
proneness to imaginary illness and hypochondria. An over-
controlled attitude towards the body constitutes the third
type of reaction. This denies the body its proper autonomy
as the person concerned feels he must be in full control.
In contrast to the hypochondriac, he cannot afford to admit
to even minor forms of ill health and he denies more serious
illness for as long as possible.

Living with disability

Although in an earlier section we differentiate between disability and handicap, implicit in our discussion is the fact
that disability of any importance usually results in some
form of handicap. Living with disability is therefore influenced by the degree to which handicap can be minimised.
    Greater factual knowledge within society about different
disabilities – their causes and effects, and also about the
restrictions they impose and how some of these can be overcome – is an important antidote against fear and prejudice.
In this context such formal measures as the International
Year of Disabled People have their value in providing a
forum for an open discussion of disabilities and for encouraging contacts between disabled people and the non-disabled.
    There are a number of specialist societies and self-help
groups which serve an important function in carrying out
research and disseminating information about specific disabilities. They also provide a valuable source of support
and encouragement to disabled people, many of whom experience considerable ambivalence themselves about the extent
to which they wish to be accepted by wider society and yet
desire the more protected environment of specialist groups
and activities.

However difficult and restricted the lives of many disabled people are, one must not overlook the great strides which have been made in recent years in helping their social functioning. Some of these have been in the realm of public attitudes and the provision of social services (although there is still a tendency to underestimate seriously the capacity of many disabled people). What we wish to emphasise in this section are the many technological achievements: some of these have literally made living possible, but many more have had a dramatic effect on the quality of life. Increased mobility as a result of adaptations to cars, better-designed wheelchairs and improved prostheses, sophisticated methods of communication, including electronic devices, and development of aids to the maintenance of organ functioning such as pacemakers (electrical devices inserted into the chest wall to control disorders of heart rhythm) and respirators, are examples of progress in this direction.

Reference is made below to some of the conditions in which the provision of good technical aids is particularly important.

Renal failure

The kidneys, like the liver, play an essential part in maintaining the chemical and physical working of the whole body: partly, but not entirely, by regulating the amount of water, salts like sodium and potassium, and waste products excreted from the bloodstream.

The kidneys may fail in their function because their outflow through the ureters, bladder and urethra is obstructed (as when the prostate gland is grossly enlarged) or through disease in their substance (as in acute glomerulo-nephritis or when there have been repeated infections of the urinary tract, involving the kidneys as well as the bladder) or when the blood passing through them is reduced in pressure or altered in chemical content (as in severe heart failure).

Failure of kidney function, if acute, will show itself as reduction in volume or absence of any urine passed. Dangerous illness rapidly follows. If slow ('chronic'), the leading symptoms are lethargy, irritability, nausea, hiccough and an itching skin. The basis for these symptoms may be difficult to detect at an early stage unless blood tests are done for electrolyte, urea and creatinine levels.

Renal dialysis and transplantation of a kidney from a

donor have changed the outlook for many sufferers from acute and chronic renal failure, when this is due to disease in the substance of the kidney. Unfortunately not all those who could benefit from these measures actually do so, an illustration of the present position in which science and medicine offer possibilities of help for people which the National Health Service cannot finance without depriving other people with other needs.

There are about 2,500 patients on chronic haemodialysis in the United Kingdom and about 2,000 with functioning transplanted kidneys. Dialysis is more often carried out at home than in hospital, but it is a tedious and stressful process which disrupts the life of the patient and his family. Although usually compatible with working, it is liable to a number of complications and carries a reduced expectation of life. Successful transplantation of the kidney is a better solution because it permits a normal mode of life, but only about two out of three patients with transplanted kidneys survive for five years.

Gastro-intestinal disorders

Many gastro-intestinal disorders run a chronic course which cannot be completely altered by treatment. They therefore create a disability, even if it may be obvious only to the patient.

Some disorders can be relieved only by forms of surgery which inevitably involve closing the anus and creating a new opening in the abdominal wall through which faeces can be passed. If this opening is an outlet for the lower bowel, it is called a 'colostomy'; if for the small bowel, an 'ileostomy'. Colostomy is the more usual, and the commonest reason for it is that part of the colon contained a malignant growth. Removing this and the neighbouring part of the bowel can sometimes be achieved without an artificial opening, but the anatomical position may sometimes make it unavoidable. The faeces drain into a plastic bag which adheres to the abdominal wall, but which has to be emptied at regular intervals. It is invisible under the clothes, but requires great effort if it is to be free from unpleasant smells. A colostomy is always unacceptable at first, and requires a major adjustment in attitude, but many patients eventually settle to the new regime very successfully.

Blindness

Partial blindness is far more common than total; it is usually associated with old age, results from degeneration of the
macula (the central part of the retina), cataract in the lens
(although this is usually treatable by surgery), or glaucoma
(raised pressure within the ball of the eye). Total blindness may date from birth, e.g. due to abnormal development
in the uterus, or may result from injury, infections or disease.
The problems of living with blindness will differ according to whether a person has known normal vision or never
been able to see at all. Having had sight even for a short
period normally makes adaptation easier, although the
devastating sense of loss may counterbalance this.
The usual means of correction of visual defect by spec-
tacles is of limited value in helping the common causes of
deteriorating sight in old age. The simple measures of
strong lighting closely applied and the use of magnifiers are
important aids in these circumstances. When large print
books (available from public libraries) become unreadable,
the radio and a supply of talking books become increasingly
important, as does the ready availability of a person to read
aloud.
Total blindness, especially in the young, means special
education, most probably including the use of Braille. In
spite of the obvious restrictions, a number of blind people
are in open employment: others need sheltered working conditions. Aids to mobility play a crucial part in determining
the independence of blind people and of these the development of the 'long cane' technique and the use of guide dogs
are the most effective at present.

Deafness

As with blindness, partial deafness is much more common
than total. It is to be seen in children in association with
ear infections, being usually transient, but sometimes leaving permanent reduction of hearing. A gradual reduction
of hearing in the second half of life is so common as to be
almost normal, but it seldom becomes total.
Complete or partial deafness can be from birth and its
detection at as early an age as possible makes routine surveillance of infants and young children essential. Later in

life, the rare conditions of otosclerosis (treatable by
operation) and Menière's disease can lead to total deafness.
Menière's disease produces the combination of deafness
with continuous noises ('tinnitus') and attacks of rotary
giddiness.

There are many designs of hearing aid available and their
effectiveness for many types of deafness is constantly
improving. They can be of great value to the partially deaf,
although none is completely satisfactory when many people
are talking together; they are most helpful in a one-to-one
conversation. Old people in particular find them difficult,
and it is therefore important to introduce them before the
capacity to adjust to their use is lost and to ensure that
skilled training in their use is made available.

Total deafness from birth or early childhood is a major
disability because it not only affects hearing, but also
speech and language development and thus cognitive thought.
It requires special education from an early age, and if not
available locally will entail boarding facilities, adding
further to family problems.

Not all deaf school leavers can develop sufficient verbal
skills to obtain employment. Lip-reading skills are therefore an important asset and sign language is a valuable
means of communication in settings where it is understood.
Since social isolation is the main handicapping element in
deafness, greater familiarity with 'signing' among the general public and relevant social services would be a welcome
development.

The contribution of social work

An important function of social work with the chronically
sick and the disabled is to identify the various handicapping
factors and to assess their significance with a view to
action.

Under the Chronically Sick and Disabled Persons Act
1970, Local Authority Social Services Departments are
responsible for the provision of a variety of services to
those covered by the Act. These include hostels, day care,
domiciliary services, various aids to living such as telephones, special gadgets and adaptations and structural
alterations to the home, e.g. to make the use of a wheelchair possible. These many statutory provisions for dealing with environmental handicapping factors are not, how-

ever, always implemented either because of shortage of resources or a lack of imagination. A major criticism of the 1970 Act is that its generous spirit was not matched by a realistic supply of the necessary means to implement it.

In the realm of financial provision, the number of different benefits available to disabled people is considerable. (5) Their applicability to an individual depends on a number of factors, including the following: the cause of the disability (e.g. pensions for the war disabled are much more generous than for those whose disabilities have been caused by injury or illness); age; whether the person has been in employment or not; degree of mobility; how much looking after he requires. Given the complexity of the picture, it is hardly surprising that many disabled people are not aware of all the benefits to which they are entitled. One of the important tasks of the social worker is, therefore, to ensure that unnecessary financial deprivation is not being experienced by the client.

In the case of many disabilities, an adequate meeting of the environmental, mobility and other needs of the client can only be achieved by bringing in appropriate specialist resources, such as those of occupational therapy, mobility training, teaching of Braille, and special communication skills in relation to deafness. Ensuring that such skills are at the client's disposal is an equally important part of the social work task.

Another essential and a distinctive contribution by social work to the well-being of chronically sick and disabled people and their families relates to the areas of family relationships and life style.

Reference was made in Chapter 4 to the often devastating effects on parents of the birth of a disabled child; the effects of disability in later life can be equally traumatic on both its victims and their families. The sudden onset of a disability produces a classic 'crisis situation' to which all the principles of 'crisis intervention' will apply.

Where a disability is of a static nature, the person once he has come to terms with what has been lost will be free to engage in life in accordance with his remaining capacities. A more difficult situation faces those whose disabilities entail a gradual loss of function and who have, therefore, to make constant adaptations to their life style.

One general assertion which in the light of both theoretical knowledge and practical experience seems justified is that no proper adaptation to a disability is possible without

first coming to terms with the loss it represents. It is
therefore of the utmost importance to allow, and even to
encourage, chronically sick and disabled people to mourn
their lost or ill-functioning organ and the effects of this,
before expecting them to be in a position to engage in rehabilitative work. Efforts at the latter, if forced upon the
disabled person prematurely, are likely to be counter-
productive, and prove harmful.

It is therefore important to recognise the less tangible
and the more metaphysical needs of disabled people on the
lines shown in the following quotation:

Many disabled people have to make a social adjustment to
cope with poverty or loss of employment and some have to
make an existential adjustment to cope with a disability
which alters their appearance. Fortunately these
aspects of disability are now more widely recognised and
are better managed by public and professionals, although
there are still many deficiencies. There is, however,
one metaphysical aspect of disability which is less frequently recognised than it was and is now less well
managed than formerly and that is the confusion which
many individuals feel about the meaning of their suffering.

'Why me?' 'I've led a good life - why should I suffer?'
'It doesn't seem fair.' This is the type of question which
perplexes many disabled people and if they are not helped
to reach an answer to this type of question the emotional
and physical consequences may increase the person's
suffering. To the Christian, and I meet many disabled
elderly Christians in the course of my work, the problem is particularly perplexing because they have to cope
with what seems to be a paradox - the God of Love who
allows suffering.... Unfortunately many of the doctors
nurses, social workers and the other professionals whom
they meet either do not even consider this aspect of disability or, if they perceive the problem, prefer not to
discuss it because religion embarrasses and perplexes
the professional whose practice is based on scientific
principles. Even if the professional is himself religious,
he may not be able to combine religion and science in his
work.

If the disabled person is not helped to answer the question 'Why me?' the effects may be severe. Anger and
resentment may result if the disease is felt to be 'unfair';
anxious agitation, if the suffering seems pointless, and

guilt and depression if the person should come to the
conclusion that his suffering is a just retribution for some
past sin. Guilt is often cited as a symptom of depression,
but depression may be a consequence of guilt.... (6)

TERMINAL ILLNESS

The problem of death in our society

'The test of the Health Service and of those who work in it
is not only how best to prevent illness and to keep people
alive and healthy, but also how to let them die with dignity
and in peace', from a symposium on the care of the dying. (7)
    'Death is just a moment when dying ends.' Montaigne
    These views of death show dying to be a process. If
taken to its logical conclusion it would entail the recognition
that dying begins at birth. It is certainly true that fear of
impending death and the progress of a lethal disease are not
always directly related. Some individuals have this fear
before the onset of any serious or disturbing physical symptoms, and others appear to refuse to recognise that they are
dying in the face of very advanced pathology. It also
seems true that a death can be 'willed' when the desire for
living has ceased, whatever the reason.
    However, for the purpose of daily practice by most doc-
tors and social workers it is not necessary to confront the
ultimate philosophical implications of 'death begins at birth',
in order to accept that dying is a process rather than an
event. To recognise this helps us to realise that dying is
a human experience which engages all the human faculties:
the body, the mind and the psyche or soul. Therefore, to
treat dying in predominantly biological terms and in isolation from its personal and social context is to dehumanise
the individual who is approaching death.
    This assertion is in many ways so obvious that the value
of saying it may well be questioned. And yet both literature
on dying and much everyday experience indicate that the
treatment not infrequently received by dying people and their
next of kin reflects either a profound ignorance of this truth
or its determined denial. Why then this striking discrepancy between the intellectual understanding of the needs of
the dying and its practical application?
    An adequate answer to this question demands a considera-
tion of certain features of our civilisation and of their

influence upon attitudes towards death and dying. One of
these is fear. Whilst fear of death is to some extent a
universal human phenomenon, its degree and manifestations
are nevertheless in many respects unique to Western socie-
ties. Gorer (8) among others has emphasised the lengths
to which the denial of the reality of death is taken.

Why should death, a natural phenomenon, be so feared in
a society which includes its commitment to rationality among
its many achievements? One explanation for this may be
that the faith in scientific and technological progress which
for many has replaced religious faith has led to a lessened
acceptance of the inevitability of death. Death is experienced as a threat to and a violation of man's powers over
the universe. His resulting inability to face the human situation realistically prevents constructive responses being
adopted.

The 'conspiracy of silence' which is a common manifestation of the need to deny death's reality provides a clear
instance of damaging effects. When death is unmentionable,
the dying person is denied the opportunity to share his most
meaningful thoughts and feelings with those who are close to
him and in consequence, he is denied the understanding,
companionship and support which he needs so badly in this
final stage of his life. Denial of these opportunities constitutes a violation of his basic human rights as well as a denigration of his intrinsic dignity, which includes the courage
and integrity needed to face up to dying. It is certainly
also a breach of the recommendations of the Parliamentary
Assembly of the Council of Europe on the Rights of the Sick
and the Dying. (9) These include the exhortation '... to
ensure that all persons have the opportunity to prepare
themselves psychologically to face the fact of death....'

Medical attitudes towards the terminally ill

Doctors vary greatly in the extent to which they are prepared to discuss fully and honestly with their dying patients
about their condition. These variations reflect partly their
own feelings about death. 'Every time we assist someone
who is dying we have to face the certainty of our own death,
and our uncertainty as to its time and manner'. (10)
Although spoken from the social-work perspective, what
was said seems equally applicable to doctors.

It would be quite unrealistic to expect a doctor who has

failed to come to terms with his own mortality to be able to assist his patients in facing up to their deaths. The prevalent culture in most medical schools and health care institutions provides little encouragement to doctors to confront the reality of death. The emphasis is still very much on the 'cure' aspects of medicine at the expense of both 'alleviation' and 'support'. This is reflected in the organisation of health care which, on the whole, fails to reflect the type of response which terminally ill people require.

According to recent statistics, approximately two-thirds of all deaths take place in hospitals. Of these the great majority occur in general hospitals. The number of places in hospitals (or hospices, as they are often called) specially designed to look after terminally ill patients, although rising, are still very few. General hospitals, with a few exceptions, are ill equipped to meet the needs of this group of patients. Their primary focus is on the treatment of acute illness and they are mostly geared to a quick turnover of patients. Their major single failing is frequently the withdrawal of active commitment, particularly in the emotional sense, from those patients who are judged to be beyond help by any criterion of curability.

Dying patients soon sense this withdrawal of interest, even when it is not manifest in such crude expressions as their beds being by-passed during ward rounds. Although no explicit reason is given to them for this, they themselves are usually well aware of it, even if they keep such knowledge to themselves out of a sense of delicacy and loyalty towards those caring for them. It hardly needs emphasising what an additional burden such an enforced silence imposes upon people, who are thus called upon to expend their limited energies on protecting those whose job it ought to be to support them at this most difficult time. Patients themselves are a product of their culture and they too fear death and are in great need of sharing their doubts and apprehensions with understanding fellow human beings.

Relatives of dying patients are usually told the diagnosis and are given some indication of the prognosis. They are not infrequently advised however to keep such information secret from the patient himself 'to spare him unnecessary anxiety'. Even when such explicit advice has not been given, relatives will often collude with the hospital staff's reluctance to 'upset' patients. In addition, relatives often feel inadequate to handle the knowledge of death without some help. The inevitable result of this 'conspiracy of

silence' is a degree of breakdown of communication
between the dying person and his next of kin.

People who die at home under the care of their general
practitioner are more likely to be spared the extremes of
secrecy and subterfuge, assuming that the patient and the
doctor have known each other for some time and have
developed a relationship of mutual respect and trust.
Dying at home in familiar surroundings and in the company
of one's family or friends has obvious advantages, depending on the quality of care, including relief from pain and the
expert nursing made available. Whatever the shortcomings
of general hospital care for dying patients, it usually
ensures a degree of physical comfort which is an essential
ingredient of terminal care. Only too often relatives of
persons dying at home are left to carry an excessive
burden of nursing and domestic duties to the detriment of
both themselves and the patient, including the effects of
this strain on the quality of their relationship.

In addition to regular visits by the patient's general practitioner, appropriately frequent visits by a community
nurse, sufficient assistance with domestic work, and the
provision of some relief at night, are the necessary requi-
sites of terminal care at home. Without these the main
raison d'être for the dying person remaining in or returning
to his own home can easily be negated.

Generalised statements about where it is better to die –
at home or at hospital – are of a limited value, as is the
case with most other generalisations about responses to
human needs. An understanding of a particular individual's
needs at a particular time is always called for. It is sad
nevertheless that for so many the choice of dying at home is
at present not available, either because they have no close
relatives or because the network of supportive services
based in the community is inadequate.

The needs of the dying

The nature of terminal illness and the extent to which it has
progressed are two important variables. These will
determine the location of pain or discomfort experienced by
the patient and its severity, and therefore also the nature
of medical help and of nursing care required. Contrary to
many lay people's expectations, pain is not a necessary
accompaniment of all terminal illness, even illness caused

by cancers. Dr Cecily Saunders, who has pioneered
much of the medical care of terminally ill people, is of the
opinion that nausea is a more common distressing and intractable symptom of terminal illness than pain. (11)
Where pain is troublesome, however, expert assistance
with its relief is of a crucial importance.

There is every reason to use powerful drugs such as
heroin (diamorphine), which seldom fails to relieve temporarily the most severe pains. The use of effective pain-
relief is often delayed too long. Pain is increased both by
the fear of it and by the experience of it. When vomiting
interferes with swallowing injections are needed. This is
one of the reasons why frequent or continuous attendance of
a skilled nurse is needed. Others are attention to the
pressure points on the skin and to matters of toilet. The
presence of a good nurse dan be of the greatest comfort to
patient and relatives alike. Night nursing is an important
need and much more difficult to provide at home. Its
availability often determines whether or not a terminally ill
person can be looked after at home.

The actual death is often very peaceful, preceded by a
total or partial clouding of consciousness. Sometimes the
mind seems clear, yet free from all suffering.

For the person concerned, the easiest way to die is
during a natural sleep or instantaneously, as may happen
with a coronary thrombosis or a sudden massive internal
haemorrhage. But if death comes unheralded, the effect
on close relatives and friends is often far more damaging
than when it is preceded by an illness which allows for a
gradual preparation.

Euthanasia

In a discussion of terminal illness and of its management
some reference to the controversial subject of euthanasia
seems to be necessary.

Euthanasia or mercy killing refers to a deliberate act of
ending life, based on a judgment that allowing the natural
process of dying to take its course would cause undue
suffering to the patient and/or his next of kin. Euthanasia
is illegal in this and most other countries. The Parliamentary Assembly of the Council of Europe, in its Recommenda-
tion 779 on the rights of the sick and the dying passed in
1976, reaffirmed the status quo: 'the doctor must make

every effort to alleviate suffering, and ... he has no
right, even in cases which appear to him to be desperate,
intentionally to hasten the natural course of death.'

Those who advocate legalisation of voluntary euthanasia
(i.e. where euthanasia has been requested by the patient
prior to his reaching the terminal stage of illness) see this
as an extension of a humane approach to the problem of pain
and suffering in terminal illness. They base their views on
the following two assumptions: firstly, that severe pain and
extensive suffering in general are inevitable in much terminal illness; and secondly, that the right to individual freedom should include the right to decide when to die. Both
these assumptions are open to question. Terminal pain and
other forms of suffering need not be regarded as inevitably
beyond control by medication and the right kind of milieu.
The concept of individual freedom does not necessarily
entail freedom in absolute terms - it is possible to oppose
euthanasia on both religious and social grounds - (man is
not the sole master of his life - both God and society have a
vested interest in it, in how it is terminated as well as in
how it is lived).

Underlying much of the advocacy for voluntary euthanasia
is the fear of painful and distressing dying. An important
additional cause of fear is derived from recent scientific
and technological advances, which make possible an artificial prolongation of life with the aid of machinery which
takes over some of the vital bodily functions. Many people
dread the prospect of themselves or their nearest and dear-
est being kept alive more or less indefinitely by such means.
Rather than to be at the mercy of other people's decision,
they prefer to have their own say as to when these machines
keeping them artificially alive are to be switched off.

An excessive preoccupation with rights and power in the
context of dying overlooks the very important distinction
between death which results from not using artificial means
of prolonging life, and death which is due to deliberate
killing. The distinction between the two is of more than a
semantic interest: it raises issues of great moral significance.

Many clinical decisions by doctors involve, and have
always involved, difficult judgments, for instance, the
moment when continuation of treatment ceases to be justified
and the patient should be allowed to die without further
therapeutic interference. Such decisions, amounting to
allowing nature to take its course, are qualitatively differ-

ent from those which have to do with deliberately timed specific acts aimed at causing death, such as, for example, administering the injection of a lethal substance.

If it is the fear of artificially delayed death coupled with the fear of excessive pain rather than of death itself which underlies many of the wishes for voluntary euthanasia, then it can be argued that what is needed, far more than provision for mercy killing, is a safeguard against the abuse of scientific and technological advances and improvements in the treatment and care of terminally ill people. Progress on those lines could not fail to result in a considerable increase in most people's sense of security and trust when anticipating their own deaths or the deaths of those who are near to them. Another important reason for many people's apprehensions in contemplating their deaths is the fear that helplessness and dependence will make a heavy burden for their relatives or friends. But denial of dependence as a normal feature of human life is characteristic of our present age. Fear of it can best be diminished by confronting the real problems which hinder the provision of better terminal care. It is doubtful whether legislation of mercy killing would lead to a more serene acceptance of the reality and the inevitability of death and it is likely to cause a number of complications in the relationship between its potential subjects and its executors.

Helping terminally ill people to find their identity

To focus on identity needs may seem strange in the context of terminal illness, but this is only true if one emphasises the importance of keeping people alive and pays no attention to the quality of the life that is left to them.

If one accepts that dying is a process, one has also to accept that it has different stages and aspects and that people use what remains of their lives in different ways. Some withdraw gradually from their various involvements with things and people; others become anxious about completing important unfinished business; this may include putting right any problematic relationships with family or friends. The need which is shared by all dying people, although some express it more clearly than others, is to discover a purpose in their life and to see it as part of a continuum of human existence, rather than as an isolated, totally negative event.

This is more easily achieved in the case of those individuals whose lives, and in particular whose relationships
with other people, have provided them with tangible evidence
of their worth. Those who are only aware of their past
failure and of the opportunities they have missed may find
themselves in a truly sad predicament. This is especially
true if they are alone and lack confirmation of their importance as human beings.

Whatever their personalities and individual circumstances,
most people in facing death go through certain recognisable
phases of adjustment. These have been differently described by a number of writers such as Kuebler-Ross, (12)
Hinton, (13), Murray-Parkes, (14) and Simone de Beauvoir. (15) The latter's moving account of her mother's
dying illustrates stages which can be best termed as those
of denial, anger, bargaining, depression, resignation, and
finally acceptance. Each one of these stages can be made
easier or more difficult by the attitudes of those who are
close to the dying person. Most individuals find comfort
and support in being able to share their thoughts and feelings during each stage, but sharing depends on a positive
relationship between the terminally ill individual and those
around him. Where there is too much conflict or ambivalence, an open exchange of thoughts and feelings is not possible and the dying person may be deprived of the understanding and support of his fellow men at a time when he
needs them most.

The contribution of social work

The nature of this contribution has already been implied in
the foregoing discussion. We hope that this has succeeded
in conveying that the quality of dying is important as well
as the quality of living. Dying makes heavy demands on the
courage, trust and integrity of both those who are facing
death and those who stand by them. Its demands can also
be increased by the particular circumstances in which it is
taking place, as for example, when it occurs in hospital,
or at home without adequate support.

Implicit in the discussion of the particular difficulties
generated for dying patients and their families by the hospital setting is the recognition and importance of the contribution which hospital based social workers can make. Their
ready availability to both can be a source of considerable

comfort and support on two counts. Where other hospital
staff have withdrawn because of their feelings of helplessness and their inability to deal with them, the social
workers' presence provides a form of compensation for
their rejection. They should be prepared to assist dying
people and their next of kin in any way they can to make
some sense of their situation and to face up to their impending loss.

A necessary condition for social workers being able to
fulfil these functions is, however, their own ability to
accept the inevitability of death and be realistic about the
uncertainties associated with it. Some social workers are
reluctant to engage in work with terminally ill patients
unless they can be sure that these patients have been fully
informed of their diagnosis and prognosis. Such an attitude frequently conceals a rather naive view of terminal
illness and a very limited understanding of the needs of
dying patients. It certainly reveals a lack of appreciation
of the complexity of human communication and the limitations
inherent in purely verbal communication.

Questions such as 'what', 'when' and 'how' should a terminally ill person be told about his condition are very complex and no general answer is possible. There should certainly be no place for crude and generalised solutions such
as withholding certain truths from patients at all costs and
telling them lies; or at the other extreme sharing brutal
facts indiscriminately and without due regard to the individual patient's readiness to accept them or to the form in
which they would be more acceptable. The first type of
solution fails because the doctor usurps certain rights in
relation to his patient to which he is not morally entitled.
The objection to the second lies in the removal of hope from
the dying person; for this he has a need as long as he is
alive – to remove it is an act of cruelty.

The steps between these two unwarranted extremes are
many. The approach adopted must relate to the needs of
the individual at a particular time and these can be gauged
from that individual only, and by no other means. Dr
Cecily Saunders has repeatedly emphasised this point: 'The
real truth is not what do you tell your patients, but rather
what do you let your patients tell you. Learn to hear what
they are saying, what they are not saying, what is hidden
underneath, what is going on.' (16)

To go back to the general hospital setting, social workers
should be the people who are most ready to hear what dying

patients are saying and what they are not saying; what
they already know (which is by no means the same as what
they have been told); what questions they want answered and
which ones they are not yet ready to ask.   Provided their
relationships with doctors and nurses are based on mutual
trust and respect, social workers can share their understanding with these colleagues, who can in this way be
helped to gear their own responses more appropriately to
their patients' needs.

Both psychological support and help with practical problems to their family are as important as direct work with
these patients.   If the family feels understood and receives
support, it is more able to respond to the needs of the
member who is dying and, by giving them opportunity to express and share their feelings about the dying person and
the approaching loss, a good deal of suffering may be
avoided.   This makes the acceptance of the actual death
much easier.   It is especially important in cases where the
relationship between the dying patient and his next of kin
contains a good deal of ambivalence and unresolved conflicts.

Our references so far to the social work contribution
within the hospital setting are equally applicable to other
settings, including that of the patient's own home.   One
would expect that in the latter, collaboration with his general practitioner would be particularly close and derived
from shared understanding of his needs and the needs of his
family.   The other important people with whom the social
worker should aim to liaise and collaborate include community nurses and, where appropriate, clergy.

A very important aspect of the social worker's contribution to terminal care at home which does not apply in the
hospital setting is the mobilisation of a variety of aids and
services.   These may range from additional funds to pay
for invalid food or extra nursing, to arrangements for incontinence laundry service or the borrowing of home nursing equipment from the British Red Cross Society.

One considerable advantage of caring for terminally ill
people in their own home setting is the greater flexibility
and informality which provide opportunities to work with
the whole family.   Such work has considerable preventive
value in terms of facilitating normal mourning by the
patient's family and safeguarding them against pathological
grief after his death.   The risk and the effects of the
latter seem to be implicit in the findings of a study (17) that

the likelihood of the nearest relation dying within the year
of bereavement was twice as great if the death that was
mourned had occurred in hospital rather than at home.

SUGGESTIONS FOR FURTHER READING

On chronic sickness and disability

D.M. Boswell and J.M. Wingrove (eds), 'The Handicapped
Person in the Community', Open University Books.
D.M. Boswell (1975), 'A Handicapped Identity', Open Uni-
versity Books
J. Campling (ed.) (1981), 'Images of Ourselves: Women with
Disabilities Talking', Routledge & Kegan Paul.
B. Wright (1960), 'Physical Disability – A Psychological
Approach', Harper & Row.
M. Blaxter (1976), 'The Meaning of Disability', Heinemann.
S. Fischer (1973), 'Body Consciousness', Calder & Boyars.
J. McDaniel (1969), 'Physical Disability and Human Behav-
iour', Pergammon.
E. Goffman (1969), 'Stigma', Penguin.
P. Hunt (ed.) (1966), 'Stigma', Chapman.
E.J. Miller and G.C. Gwynne (1974), 'A Life Apart',
Tavistock.
Disability Alliance (1979), 'Disability Rights Handbook',
Disability Alliance.
Central Council for the Education and Training in Social
Work (1974), 'People with Handicaps need Better Trained
Social Workers', CCETSW.

On terminal illness

J. Hinton (1967), 'Death', Penguin.
E. Kuebler-Ross (1970), 'On Death and Dying', Tavistock.
C. Murray-Parkes (1972), 'Bereavement: Studies in Grief
in Adult Life', Tavistock.
L. Pincus (1976), 'Death and the Family', Faber.
C. Saunders (ed.) (1978), 'The Management of Terminal
Disease', Arnold.

Chapter 8

Health care settings

INTRODUCTION

So far we have largely focused on the nature of health
problems and on appropriate responses to these by doctors
and social workers. In this chapter we shall examine
some of the major characteristics of the settings in which
health care is sought and offered (these play an important
part in determining the nature of the service provided).
The two most obvious settings in Britain, as in most other
countries, are primary health care or general practice, and
hospitals. These two settings are not, however, exclusive
in terms of health care, much of which takes place by means
of informal consultation with various members of local communities. We have therefore added the community as our
third health-care setting (this should not be taken to imply,
however, that we do not regard both general practice and
hospitals as belonging to the community) but, because the
major concern of this book is with the contribution of social
workers to health care, we have focused on social services
departments of local authorities as the major agency in this
context.

PRIMARY HEALTH CARE AND GENERAL PRACTICE

Primary health care is not synonymous with general practice, because it also includes care by community nurses,
health visitors, dental surgeons, industrial health departments, opticians, pharmacists, and others. The term
applies to those services to which people can choose to go
direct. It implies first contact and continuing care.

191

In Britain the general practitioner is the first port of call
for most people with health problems. As has already been
emphasised, health problems constitute a mixture of the
physical, the psychological, and the social. However, the
belief still persists among many people, some general practitioners included, that the doctor's task is to deal exclusively with physical problems. Those general practitioners
who subscribe to such a viewpoint resent being consulted
about 'non-medical' matters, arguing perhaps that the availability of 'free' health care has led to their being burdened
with too many 'extraneous' problems. However, in countries where patients pay the doctor directly, a very similar
picture prevails, i.e. a variety of social and psychological
problems are brought to the primary health-care doctor.

The ten commonest symptoms of which patients complain
to their general practitioner, in order of frequency, are: (1)

1 Cough	6 Spots and sores
2 Rashes	7 Pain in back
3 Pain in throat	8 Pain in chest
4 Pain in abdomen	9 Pain in the head
5 Disturbance of bowel function	10 Disturbance of gastric function

The six diagnoses most frequently made by general practitioners are: (2)

1 Superficial injuries
2 Upper respiratory tract infection
3 Simple anxiety and tension states
4 Contraceptive advice
5 Acute gastro-enteritis
6 Acute otitis media

Provided that he has access to X-ray and laboratory
investigations at the nearby hospital, the general practitioner, with his team, will normally deal with nine out of
ten new problems himself, referring only one to hospital.
About one in a hundred of his new problems will be admitted
to hospital as an inpatient. Thus, the notion prevalent in
the early days of the National Health Service that the general practitioner acts mainly as a signpost to hospital is at
present far from being valid. A referral by him is still,
however, a necessary prerequisite to obtaining access to a
hospital specialist - a role which invests the general practitioner with considerable power.

The extent to which he can respond adequately to the
wide range of problems brought to him depends both on his
own professional versatility, and on his ability to draw on
the services of others, including social workers.

A number of studies of social work in the general-practice
setting (e.g. Forman and Fairbairn (3) and Goldberg and
Neill (4)) have consistently shown it to be an important
catchment point for a variety of potentially serious personal
and social difficulties before they have had time to escalate
and become intransigent.

The role of the general practitioner

The essential duties of the general practitioner in primary
health care are to prevent, diagnose and treat illness, and
to care for the sick. Preventive work is increasing as
more knowledge becomes available about the cause/effect
connections in health and disease. Another developing
role is educative as awareness of the effects of people's
habits and life styles on their health increases. The general practitioner can also play an important role in his local
community. The extent of this varies, being more pronounced in villages and small towns than in large conurbations;
but even in the latter the general practitioner can be a
stable element in a rapidly changing environment. An
important example of this is his provision of continuity of
care to individuals and families, often over years. Care
forms a larger part of the general practitioner's work than
cure, because in addition to those he himself cannot cure,
he carries the additional responsibility of caring for those
whose diseases others have failed to cure.
  The general practitioner differs from doctors specialis-
ing in secondary and tertiary medicine (i.e. hospital and
specialist medicine) partly in the continuity of his presence,
partly in direct accessibility to patients, and partly
because his scope is very general and broad: he has to
make at least an initial decision in the face of each problem
the patient presents, and will often be asked to deal with
different sorts of problems in the same person, sometimes
simultaneously. To assess which is most important or
urgent is therefore a continuous responsibility. He may be
asked to deal with problems in different members of a
family, it being usual for at least the nuclear family to
register with the same doctor.
  This description of a general practitioner's role is uni-
versally applicable in Britain but is not necessarily correct
for other countries. However, there are a number of
important common features of the role of a doctor in primary

health care which transcend national frontiers, and it is
this which has enabled a working party from twelve European countries to produce a policy document acceptable to
doctors in the European Community who work in general
practice. The following definition of general practice
comes from this source:

> The general practitioner is a licensed medical graduate
> who gives personal, primary and continuing care to indi-
> viduals, families and a practice population, irrespective
> of age, sex and illness. It is the synthesis of these
> functions which is unique. He will attend his patients in
> his consulting room and in their homes and sometimes in
> a clinic or a hospital. His aim is to make early diag-
> noses. He will include and integrate physical, psycho-
> logical and social factors in his considerations about
> health and illness. This will be expressed in the care
> of his patients. He will make an initial decision about
> every problem which is presented to him as a doctor.
> He will undertake the continuing management of his
> patients with chronic, recurrent or terminal illnesses.
> Prolonged contact means that he can use repeated oppor-
> tunities to gather information at a pace appropriate to
> each patient and build up a relationship of trust which he
> can use professionally. He will practise in co-opera-
> tion with other colleagues, medical and non-medical. He
> will know how and when to intervene through treatment,
> prevention and education to promote the health of his
> patients and their families. He will recognise that he
> also has a professional responsibility to the community. (5)

The location of general practice

Some general practitioners work on their own from their
own homes, or at a rented surgery, but most now practise
in partnership with others, usually sharing premises.
Whether or not midwives, nurses, health visitors, geriatric
visitors or social workers are included in the health-care
team varies, but the trend in the last fifteen years has been
towards more multi-disciplinary teams.

Since the inception of the National Health Service, official policy has encouraged general practitioners to join in
group practices and to operate from a health centre base.
A health centre is not easily distinguished from a group
practice based on its own premises. Strictly defined, a

health centre is a building which belongs either to the local authority or the National Health Service and which, besides general practitioners and their receptionists, accommodates other health care personnel.

Whatever the location of the doctor, his membership of a group practice usually means that the patient who telephones him or goes to see him will come first in contact with a receptionist. If there is an appointment system the receptionist holds a position of some power, but in any case hers is a difficult job, caught as she is between patients and doctor. This role, which is normally a busy one, requires considerable skill, tolerance and tact, as well as efficiency. Although there are training courses for doctors' receptionists, most will have learnt their task on the job. Many receptionists are held in high regard by patients and become the recipients of their confidences.

There are no firmly established criteria by which to judge the overall advantages of single-handed versus group practices, small or large. Undoubtedly, the closest personal relationship between patient and doctor is favoured by the single-handed practice, but the doctor is then relatively isolated from colleagues doing the same type of work, and he has also more difficulty in arranging off-duty periods. He is less likely to have adequate reception arrangements and secretarial assistance, and his ability to collaborate with others on behalf of his patients will tend to suffer. In 1974 only 18 per cent of doctors were single-handed. (6)

Group practice tends to weaken the links between a particular doctor and his patients, but it enables the sharing of receptionists, secretaries and equipment, and the organisation of off-duty periods. Its most important advantage is mutual stimulation and criticism between colleagues, but this only applies if the members of a group meet regularly to discuss clinical as well as organisational problems. Group practice, whether in a health centre or not, makes the attachment of nurses, health visitors and social workers easier and it also lends itself to visits by medical specialists. It is a form of organisation of general practice which is encouraged and supported by a financial inducement.

The primary health-care team

According to Department of Health and Social Security
statistics, (7) in 1973 77 per cent of the 11,970 'home
nurses' were attached to general practitioners, and of the
8,172 health visitors, 79 per cent were so attached. The
figures for nurses do not include those directly employed by
general practitioners as surgery nurses: although the
absolute numbers of these are not known, they have increased. There is a great variation in the different parts
of the country and far fewer single-handed practitioners
have nursing and health-visitor attachments than is the
case in group practices.

   Although the value of a multi-disciplinary approach in
primary health care is in principle widely recognised,
many general practitioners have serious reservations and
experience personal difficulties in delegating work to
nurses and health visitors. (8) Relationships with the
latter in particular are often fraught with difficulties, and
in spite of more attachments since 1960, there are still
many general practitioners who fail to see their value.
This has prompted many health visitors to express a preference for basing their work on a geographical area.
Whilst traditionally health visitors were primarily concerned with the health care of children under 5, in recent
years they have extended their role to include people over
65. (9) Geriatric health visitors, who specialise in dealing with old people, are of considerable help to general
practitioners in maintaining regular contact with a group of
people who, as we have indicated in Chapter 4, tend to
lose contact with the medical services and neglect health
problems for which effective help is available.

   Full-time attachment of social workers to general practice is still uncommon. Whether or not this becomes more
general in future, depends on a number of factors, including the attitude of general practitioners towards a social
work input into primary health care and the perception on
the part of social workers as to how they should be
deployed. Ratoff, on the basis of the studies of social work
attachments already referred to (Forman and Fairbairn (10)
and Goldberg and Neill (11)) categorises the functions
undertaken by social workers in general practices as
follows:

   (1) social assessment and evaluation - a diagnostic
        service;

(2) casework – a therapeutic service;
(3) resource mobilisation, provision of services and referral – a liaison service;
(4) educational work with patients, students and colleagues. (12)

The organisation of the general practitioner's work and the system of his remuneration

The general practitioner in Britain has a list of patients who register with him. He is responsible for their health care for 24 hours every day throughout the year, but this responsibility can be delegated. Sharing of duty hours is clearly easier in the context of a group practice, but where general practitioners practise singly they can enter into an arrangement with a deputising service. General practitioners vary greatly in the extent to which they use such a service: some have been criticised for resorting to it excessively to the detriment of continuity of care, and there is now a statutory limit to such 'contracting out'.

The average list size of general practitioners is now about 2,300 patients, but this covers a range from 1,700 to 4,500. There has been a good deal of debate about what constitutes the optimum number of patients for a general practitioner's list but no firm conclusion has been reached. A recent study by Butler (13) has shown that individual doctors vary considerably in what they consider to be the right size for a list, and also that there is no evidence for a simple connection between the number of patients on a doctor's list and the quality of health care they receive.

A small number of patients make up a disproportionate number of a general practitioner's work. Courtenay noted that 26 per cent of patients created 61 per cent of practice consultations. (14) 25 per cent of urgent requests were made by 3 per cent of Forbes's practice. (15)

Apart from surgery consultations and home visits, general practitioners spend time on the telephone, on paper work and 'on call'. In 1967–8, the average working week was 39 hours (range 26–53 hours) with a further 76 hours 'on call'. (16) Most general practitioners are called out after they go to bed once every two or three weeks, but this does not apply to those who regularly use a deputising service.

Few general practitioners totally confine their work to providing general medical services under the National

Health Service. Private practice, work for insurance companies, or for the police, are examples of additional work undertaken. Nevertheless, the great majority of general practitioners derive most of their income from their National Health Service payments, and less than 5 per cent work completely outside the National Health Service.

The term 'independent contractor' applies to all general practitioners, as none of them are fully salaried. At the beginning of the National Health Service, the method of payment was a standard annual sum for each patient on a general practitioner's list - a 'capitation fee' - without regard to the age of the patient or frequency of consultations. After thirty years the system has become much more complicated and the general practitioner is now paid in almost equal parts by salary, capitation fee and item of service.

There is much to be said for a system which balances the advantages and disadvantages of each method. Regretfully, however, the present system still fails to encourage high quality. One real obstacle is the absence of reliable and agreed criteria for judging quality. On balance, the authors' impression from their travels in other countries is that the British system, with all its drawbacks, is at least as good as any to be found elsewhere.

Attitudes of general practitioners to their work

Twenty-five years ago, two-thirds or more of general practitioners would have preferred a specialist career in medicine - general practice was at best a second choice for most. In the last two years there has been a clear shift in career choice of final year medical students towards general medical practice. A younger generation of general practitioners are now coming into practice who have had a specific training for their work, after making a positive choice for this branch of medicine.

Social workers will be aware of the varying attitudes of general practitioners towards their patients. Cartwright's work provides valuable information on this. (17)

Most general practitioners find that patients with psychiatric or social problems present the greatest challenge. This includes alcoholics, schizophrenics, people with marital conflicts and adolescents. Apart from their inherent difficulties, these problems demand more time than is easily found and they call for knowledge and skills of a type which has only recently been included in medical education.

Like all doctors, general practitioners vary in the extent
to which they subscribe to a holistic view of medicine. The
more 'organically minded' they are, the more frustrated
they are likely to feel at having to give their time and attention to 'non-medical' problems. The difficulties are com-
pounded, if their own reluctance to respond to this type of
problem is accompanied by unwillingness or inability to
involve others, including social workers, with their
patients.

Training for general practice

Until recently, a medical student was considered to be fit
to practise as a general practitioner when he had completed
six years at medical school and one year of obligatory hospital experience as a house-physician or house-surgeon.
Almost the whole training was hospital- and specialist-
oriented. In the last ten years a three-year training
planned for intending general practitioners has been
designed and this is now undertaken by those wishing to
enter this branch of medicine. It takes place partly in
hospital, partly in specially selected teaching practices,
and partly on courses; it has a psycho-social orientation
to counter-balance a basic training still biased towards
physical disorders.
It has been demonstrated that this three-year course
influences attitudes in young doctors, but there is not, as
yet, an objective study relating this training to subsequent
practice. The problem of identifying and measuring
quality makes such a study very difficult. In spite of the
fact that it postpones the time of independent responsibility
by three years to a total of ten, a higher proportion of the
best students than in the past now choose a career in general practice.

The quality of care in general practice

In a service where the individual doctor is mainly responsible only to his patients and has few statutory duties,
where there is no hierarchy and only light control 'from
above', there are bound to be wide differences in practice
behaviour. These discrepancies are further increased by
the fact that there still are a number of general practitioners

who work singly and in relative isolation from their fellows. In these circumstances it is inevitable that there are differing degrees of quality in the care provided. There are three major obstacles to equalising and raising standards: lack of agreement about what constitutes high quality primary health care and what its objectives should be; lack of proper methods for measuring the degree to which objectives are attained; lack of acceptance by all but a few of the doctors that they have a dual obligation to examine their own standards and to have them examined by others.

Some valuable work has been done by medical sociologists (e.g. Cartwright) (18) on evaluating general practice by the use of consumer survey methods. However, satisfaction by consumers alone is not a sufficient measure of the quality of care. Consumers are not necessarily the best judges, being often unaware of what medicine has to offer and of the criteria for the use of different therapeutic measures. These have shown both a high degree of satisfaction with the service received and an inherent difficulty by patients to be critical of their doctors.

The increasing interest in all developed countries in the question of ensuring quality in medical care and in its measurement is stimulated by two major factors: the ever-rising costs of medical care and the increasing awareness of health being 'everybody's business' and of the resulting necessity to involve others, besides doctors, in its promotion.

If the objectives of primary health care could be agreed, and acceptable methods for the measurement of its quality devised, improvements in many areas would undoubtedly follow. However for this to become possible, doctors must involve themselves in a co-operative effort for scrutiny of their work and shed some of their present reluctance to expose themselves to evaluation. If this were to happen, they would set an important example of responsible accountability to match the authority and trust vested in them.

HOSPITALS

Some major characteristics of the hospital setting

Hospitals have gradually over many years become places primarily concerned with the diagnosis and treatment of serious illnesses. This is in contrast to their former

functions during the period of pre-scientific medicine,
when the provision of rest and care predominated, hence
the frequent use of 'hospice' in their title.

Modern hospitals bring together powerful resources,
both in professional personnel with different skills and in
complex technical equipment. At their best they perform
fine feats of teamwork. They are especially suited to deal
effectively with the investigation and treatment of major
physical disorders, frequently achieving dramatic results
which could not be obtained by lesser means. They continue to provide care when illness is too great a burden for
relatives to carry or when none exist. They are, however,
extremely expensive to run and are liable to the many disadvantages common to large and complicated institutions.

Hospitals are inevitably frightening to patients and to
their families. Some people are admitted to them as emer-
gencies following a sudden illness (e.g. coronary occlusion)
or an accident. Such admissions are highly dramatic and
traumatic events, often more so for the family than for the
patient; he himself is likely to be too ill to react strongly
to what is happening to him. More commonly a person
comes to hospital after a planned referral by his own
doctor. This implies the possibility of a serious illness
which the examination and tests made by the general practitioner either did not exclude or suggested as likely. Such
a possibility in itself provokes anxiety in most people and
the resulting uncertainty can be prolonged, depending on
the type of investigations required.

The time-lag between the referral of a person by his
general practitioner to a hospital specialist and the date of
the first outpatient appointment varies considerably,
depending on a number of factors, of which the geographical
location, the nature of the speciality and the urgency of the
patient's condition are the chief ones.

The result of the first hospital consultation is usually
from the patient's viewpoint relatively uninformative. His
main concern is to know whether or not he is suffering
from some definite disease and what the implications of this
are for his future, but these are seldom questions to which
he can be given an answer immediately. For the doctor the
main purpose of the first consultation is to find the necessary pointers to the tests and investigations required.

The potential range of these is enormous – various laboratory tests of the blood, the urine, and the faeces; many different kinds of X-ray – from the relatively straightforward

chest X-ray to complex ones such as those which examine
the stomach and intestinal tract, kidneys or gall-bladder.
Direct inspection of internal organs through the appropriate
body orifices (e.g. bronchoscopy, cystoscopy or sigmoido-
scopy) is another possible type of procedure. Some of
these investigations are very unpleasant and even painful.
To new patients they are unknown threats, and dreaded
events to those who have experienced them before but need
them repeated.

Hospitals vary as to whether or not they admit patients
for some of these tests, or whether they do them on an outpatient basis; increasingly, owing to the high cost of inpatient care, the latter practice is adopted. For people
who live alone or who cannot easily opt out of their normal
responsibilities (e.g. mothers of young children) this period
of investigation can be a very difficult one.

The second hospital consultation usually takes place a
few weeks after the first and it is often then that the patient
gets his 'verdict'. He is either told that the investigations
were negative and that he is free from disease or, alternatively, he is given a diagnosis and its implications for
treatment.

Whatever the news, how it is communicated is of crucial
and long-lasting significance.

Whilst most people are highly relieved at being told that
there is nothing seriously wrong with them, they also need
some recognition that their symptoms were genuine and not
imaginary. Unfortunately, some 'organically minded'
doctors still operate from the premise that a symptom such
as a pain is only genuine if it is associated with demonstrable pathology; they tend to dismiss physically unveri-
fied symptoms as 'psychosomatic', used in a derogatory
sense, rather than in the neutral and descriptive sense of
interaction between body and mind. Not surprisingly
patients dismissed in this way experience feelings of rejection and denigration which may even be greater than their
sense of relief.

Telling a person that he has a serious disease calls
equally for both kindness and skill.

Depending on the nature of the verdict and the patient's
readiness to accept and handle it, the doctor should tell him
the relevant facts by considered steps and degrees of
explicitness. The timing and the tempo of such communication should as far as possible be adjusted to the patient's
own needs and capacity, but it may well be influenced by

factors outside the doctor's control. For example, if a diagnosis of cancer of the bowel calls for immediate major surgery, then inevitably more frightening facts have to be communicated within a shorter time-span than might otherwise have been desirable.

A vital factor in communication is an exact understanding of what it is that concerns the patient most. Subjective feelings are very important in this respect, and so it is not safe to assume the presence or absence of any particular reaction in an individual. Thus some people, on being told that they require surgery, fear their chances of survival from the actual operation, whilst others are much more concerned about the degree of residual disability and its effects on their future lives.

In talking with their patients, hospital doctors, in comparison with general practitioners, suffer from the disadvantage of knowing their patients less well and being unable to draw upon an existing relationship. It is neither surprising nor inappropriate, therefore, that in many cases the task of helping a person understand and come to terms with his condition is left to his general practitioner.

People who attend a hospital as outpatients have their home base from which to draw their sense of security when faced with the strange and frightening world of white coats, mysterious machinery and depersonalised procedures; they can return to it for rest and comfort after the trials of the various investigations. For a person who is admitted as an inpatient, the hospital becomes for a time his whole world.

This can be experienced as a relief by people who have been carrying on with their responsibilities against increasing odds; for them to be looked after is a welcome change. For many people, however, the loss of their usual social roles and of the status that goes with them can be a very threatening experience. Much depends on individual circumstances, such as the nature of illness and the expected length of hospital stay, and in particular on the devotion and availability of family and friends and on how these are maintained in the face of the separation.

Hospitalisation provides most people with a severe test of the extent to which they have succeeded in establishing a reasonable balance between their needs for dependence and their capacity to be independent. Very few individuals can altogether avoid feeling threatened by the degree of enforced dependence which would normally be inappropriate for adults, whether in a physical form (e.g. having one's most

intimate bodily functions attended to by others) or a psychological form (waiting to be told what is to happen next).

The more mature and more secure an individual, the
easier he finds it to bear his change of role and status, but
even in his case the adjustment is relative rather than
absolute. Most people in their reactions to hospitalisation
tend to veer towards one of two extremes: they either
resent their state and feel angry or they relish being looked
after.

Individuals who are prone to the former type of reaction
find it particularly difficult to cope with a prolonged hospital
stay and the uncertainty about the rate and extent of their
recovery. Those who belong to the latter category have
greater problems over convalescence and they feel much
more ambivalent about resuming full responsibility for
themselves. For this group, the policy of modern hospitals
of discharging their patients at the earliest possible
moment, which accentuates the gap between physical and
psychological recovery, presents added problems.

The place of social work in hospitals

It is apparent from the above that hospitals are in many
respects daunting places for most patients, both because
they deal with life-and-death situations and because of
their structure and organisation.

Because so much human suffering can be encountered in
hospitals, they are a natural place for social work. In
fact they were one of the first public services to employ
social workers ('almoners'), although at that time their
functions were ambiguous; part of their job was to prevent
the abuse of voluntary hospital resources.

One obvious reason why hospitals provide a strategic
base for social workers is the level of crisis situations
represented there. As suggested already, for many people
referral to a hospital in itself constitutes a crisis. In
addition a large number of specific events such as operations, loss of vital body organs and functions, separation
from home and family, are classic types of crisis as
defined in literature. To deal with these effectively,
specific methods of intervention are necessary. Amongst
other things ready accessibility and concentrated help over
a relatively short span of time are essential. To be able
to offer such help the social worker must be on the spot and

part of the institution, rather than someone who calls in occasionally from outside.

Another important feature of hospital patients is that they are a group who sustain losses of many different types: of unfulfilled hopes, of social roles or important physical abilities. Here insights from dynamic psychology, including the many writings on bereavement, indicate the importance of 'mourning' as a prerequisite for satisfactory adjustment, but also the many obstacles to people being able to do this adequately. These obstacles can be particularly powerful in a hospital setting where, largely to help staff morale, keeping patients cheerful at all costs is only too prevalent a preoccupation. 'Good patients' are considered to be those who don't cry or complain and whose response to hospitalisation and treatment is placid and accepting.

Social workers are not only equipped by training to help patients 'to mourn and to support them in their work of mourning' (Freud), but they are also better placed strategically than either doctors or nurses to fulfil this function because they do not have such direct involvement in the losses sustained.

As we have already suggested in Chapter 3 this 'distance' of the social worker from medical treatment and nursing care gives him certain integral strengths for particular aspects of communication. Other things being equal, talking with a doctor may well entail more anxiety for some hospital patients than discussion with a social worker. More specifically, social workers are particularly well placed for helping patients' difficulties over their enforced dependence. These problems arise largely in relation to doctors and to nurses because of their life-giving and caring functions. Although as a result of regression, many patients' reactions to them are often subjective and irrational, it is realistically extremely difficult for doctors and nurses to combine their ministrations with active encouragement of personal autonomy. In contrast, a social worker's primary responsibility is to help an individual in his social functioning. In the hospital setting this entails helping him to accept dependence without loss of self-esteem and to maintain personal autonomy wherever possible and to make his own rational decisions. The case of Mr Harrison in Chapter 3 provides an illustration of these various points.

In addition to helping patients through crises and in adjusting to ill health and its accompanying restrictions, social workers can help to make communication between patients and staff more effective. A major task then is to get to know people as individuals by allowing time and opportunity for listening to what they reveal about their special worries and needs. The understanding gained (though not necessarily the details) should be readily shared with doctors and nurses to ease their own communications with patients, provided the latter's consent can be secured or assumed.

A necessary prerequisite to obtaining the trust of both patients and staff is for social workers to be prepared to identify themselves with the medical objectives of the hospital and to acquire relevant knowledge about the various types of diseases and their implications for personal and social life. Without this the social worker will fail to pick up many of the patients' subtler communications about their feelings, their health and their current hospital experience. Whilst much of the medical knowledge has to be obtained through experience, there is useful literature about social work with patients suffering from various types of ill health based on 'practice wisdom' and some of this is listed in the bibliography.

THE COMMUNITY SETTING AND SOCIAL SERVICES DEPARTMENTS

'Community' is notoriously difficult to define, but references to it usually include the various social networks and institutions – both formal and informal – within an identifiable geographical area (or sometimes some other entity, e.g. an ethnic community) which impinge in varying degrees upon the lives of those who live within it. Families are one of the major constituent parts of most communities and their importance in relation to health care is crucial: it is primarily and predominantly within the family setting that health is promoted or endangered and health problems are taken care of or neglected.

Many other institutions within the community are of direct relevance to health. These include statutory bodies, such as the environmental health inspectorate and a variety of voluntary agencies and self-help groups: The British Red Cross Society, Salvation Army, Gingerbread, the British Diabetic Association, Society for Mentally Handicapped Children and Adults, Alcoholics Anonymous – are but a few of these but they illustrate the range and variety.

The major community-based institution within which
social workers can make their contribution to the health
care of the community comprises the local social services
departments. The fact that these departments, however
remote they may feel to some members of a community, are
in fact an integral part of it, is borne out by the objectives
for which they were created under the recommendations of
the Seebohm Committee. (19)

Before, however, discussing more specifically the
social-work contribution within these departments, two
points need to be clarified. The first of these is that,
whilst they are the major employer of social workers in the
community setting, they are not the only base for social
work. Both probation and after-care departments and a
number of voluntary agencies employ a considerable number
of social workers, and these workers play an important
part in health matters. The other important clarification
refers to the fact that social services departments and
social work are not synonymous. The former are responsible for the provision of a large number of different services, many of which do not require a social-work involvement. In fact, social workers constitute only about 10-15
per cent of the total manpower of most of them.

Social work within social services departments

The organisational setting of the local authority social services departments is a complex one due to the multiplicity
of their functions, their large size and the resulting need
for a bureaucratic structure to ensure public accountability. This fact has been causing difficulties for social work
as a professional service since the inception of these
departments.

Whilst some of the difficulties stem from a general
ambiguity within social work about its nature and proper
functions and cannot be laid exclusively at the door of
social services departments, many are made more acute by
certain features which characterise many of them.

One such feature is the failure to determine the nature
and degree of skills required to provide the different kinds
of services for which these departments are responsible.
It is by no means infrequent for social workers, trainees,
welfare assistants and other personnel to carry identical
caseloads. Such a situation is bound to result in frustra-

tion for all these workers and consequently inefficient
service to clients. Another problem follows directly from
this: managerial control has to be geared to ensuring the
accountability of the least-skilled members of staff. This
is often inappropriate and incompatible with the degree of
responsibility which is carried by social workers. In
addition to the existence of rigid procedures, a particularly
worrying situation is created for many social workers by a
predetermined and generalised system of priorities: this
interferes with a professional approach to caseload management which must be based on a careful assessment of needs
in a particular case. As a result of such a generalised
approach, child-care problems are almost invariably given
the highest priority by management because of the legal
aspects, the publicity they attract and the potential hazards
involved. This type of work can be almost limitless: the
pressures these cases generate leave many social workers
with little or no time or energy for serious attention to other
kinds of work. Clients most likely to be neglected are those
who attract less public attention and sympathy and who do
not express their problems in dramatic and visible ways.
The chronically sick, the physically and mentally disabled
and elderly people come into this category. The following
statement made by an experienced and respected social
worker two years ago, concerning the inadequacy of many
of the services provided to old people still holds true today:
    Part of the problem lies within prevalent social work
    attitudes to the elderly, who despite consuming 50% of the
    financial resources get a small share of social work time.
    If social workers were able to show the same commitment
    and interest in the welfare of the elderly as they do for
    children in care, they could effect radical changes in the
    pattern of provision. (20)
Some restrictions with which social workers in social
services departments have to deal stem largely from the
fact that these departments, unlike hospitals or schools,
are not geared to the provision of a professional type of
service. Office conditions in which people are expected to
work are one example. The majority of social services
departments' field staff are divided into area teams, consisting usually of 8-15 social workers, plus welfare assistants and administrative and clerical workers. A team
leader is in charge and, except for him, no other social
worker is likely to have his own office. He may well share
a telephone with three or four other people, and it is not

unusual for all members of a team to be housed in one room. Such working conditions are hardly conducive to the concentration of thought and to an efficient deployment of time and energies, which are the basic requirement of all good social work. The availability of secretarial help is also often very restricted, resulting in most records having to be handwritten, which in itself discourages many people from recording adequately.

The most serious single disadvantage, however, is the absence of opportunities for continued professional development, comparable to those available, for example, in teaching and medicine. Regular guidance, geared to the needs of the young practitioner and aimed at safeguarding the interests of his clients, is lacking in many departments.

The contribution to health care of social workers based in social services departments

It is clear that many potential clients with specific health problems are deprived of social-work help under the present system of priorities in many social services departments. In addition to the individual and family social casework which would benefit many of them, a community orientation calls for much more social-work initiative and support in regard to the various self-help groups in the fields of illness and disability than is provided at present.

A crucial feature of the contribution social work can make to health care in a community is the establishment and maintenance of close links with those who have the foremost responsibility for primary health care, i.e. general practitioners. What often limits fruitful collaboration between social workers in area teams and general practitioners is that the territory and population they serve may not coincide. This means that no one social worker is likely to be in touch at any one time with more than one or two of a general practitioner's patients and that a general practitioner needs to liaise with several social workers about patients on his list.

One obvious way in which many of the current obstacles to an effective collaboration can be overcome is by attachment of social workers to general practices. This has the advantage of doctors and social workers being able to get to know each other and to evolve satisfactory ways of working together. The obstacles to this have been discussed earlier in this chapter. The low priority given in some social services departments to health problems is a further constraint. Another is the pressure of 'statutory work', coupled with a shortage of trained workers in many departments. That the problem of resources is very real is illustrated by the case of one department in southern England. There, the director was keenly interested in the establishment of closer links with the general practitioners in the area, and the latter were anxious to have social workers attached to their practices. However, when the manpower implications were worked out, on the basis of a ratio of one social worker to three general practitioners, it transpired that the department's whole social work staff would be deployed in general practice attachments, leaving none for all the other social work in the department!

It is beyond the scope of this book to consider in detail the overall shortage of social workers and their deployment in relation to function and setting. One comment, however, which we think important to make is that, in our view, the principle voiced in the 'Green Paper' on the reorganisation of the National Health Service (21) in England and Wales, and which provided the basis for the transfer of hospital social workers to the employment of social services department (as from 1 April 1974), is by no means self-evident. According to that principle, the place of employment should be determined by the nature of the skills deployed by its staff rather than by the needs or characteristics of its clientele. This can be questioned on a number of grounds, not least because it implicitly advocates a particular type of compartmentalisation and recognises insufficiently the crucial importance of inter-disciplinary practice if health care is to be perceived and provided holistically.

Attachment to general practice is, however, by no means the only way in which community-based social workers can make a valuable contribution to health. Throughout the book we have argued that there is a health component in many human problems, either as a causal factor, or as a derivative. Provided, therefore, all social workers are sensitive to health matters, they will recognise these in a variety of situations. For example, studies of so-called problem families have consistently shown that health deficiencies play an important part in these families' failure to function adequately (e.g. the Royal College of Psychiatrists sponsored study. (22)

It is because of this widespread prevalence of health

troubles in the community that we have addressed this book
largely to the generalist social worker.

SUGGESTIONS FOR FURTHER READING

Primary health care and the general practice setting

P. Pritchard (1981), 'Manual of Primary Health Care',
2nd edition, Oxford University Press.
Royal College of General Practitioners (1979), 'Trends in
General Practice'.
D. Hicks (1976), 'Primary Health Care: A Review', HMSO.
G. Bennet (1979), 'Patients and their Doctors', Balliere &
Tindall.
G. Beales (1978), 'Sick Health Centres', Pitman Medical.
G. Marsh and P. Kaim-Caudle (1976), 'Team Care in Gene-
ral Practice', Croom Helm.
A. Cartwright (1967), 'Patients and Doctors', Routledge &
Kegan Paul.
A. Cartwright and R. Anderson (1981), 'General Practice
Re-visited', Tavistock.
J.R. Butler (1980), How many Patients?, 'Occasional
Papers in Social Administration', no. 64, Bedford Square
Press.
J.A.S. Forman and E.M. Fairbairn (1968), 'Social Case-
work in General Practice', Oxford University Press.
E.M. Goldberg and J.E. Neill (1972), 'Social Work in
General Practice', Allen & Unwin.

The hospital setting

B. Abel-Smith (1964), 'The Hospitals, 1800-1948', Heine-
mann.
A. Cartwright (1964), 'Human Relations and Hospital
Care', Routledge & Kegan Paul.
I.E.P. Menzies (1970), 'The Functioning of Social Sys-
tems as a Defence against Anxiety', Tavistock Institute of
Human Relations.
Hospital Advisory Service (1971-1074), 'Annual Report',
HMSO.
H.M. Bartlett (1961), 'Some Aspects of Social Casework
in a Medical Setting', National Association of Social
Workers, N.Y.

Butrym, Z.T. (1968), 'Medical social work in action',
Occasional Papers in Social Administration, Bell & Sons.
H. Lambrick (1967), Communication with the Patient, in
'Social Work and Social Values', ed. E. Younghusband,
Allen & Unwin.
A. Hartshorn (1967), The Role of the Social Worker in the
treatment of 'Stroke' Illness, 'Medical Social Work', April.
N. McCaughan (1967), Social Work with Three Men Suffer-
ing from the Loss of a Limb, 'Medical Social Work', Septem-
ber, October.
H. Muras (1968), Medical Social Work with Patients Treated
by Renal Transplantation, 'Medical Social Work', June.
M. Willis (1969), Psychological Illness in Medical Out-
patients - Social Worker's Contribution, 'Medical Social
Work', October.
M. Chambers (1974), Some Aspects of Social Work on a
Cancer Research and Treatment Unit in a London Teaching
Hospital, 'British Journal of Social Work', vol. 4, no. 2.

The community setting

'Report of the Committee on Local Authority and Allied Per-
sonal Social Services' (Seebohm Report) (1968), HMSO.
'Report of the Working Party on Social Work Support for the
Health Service' (Otton Report) (1974), HMSO.
Department of Health and Social Security/Central Health
Services Council and Personal Social Services Council
(1978), 'Collaboration in Community Care: A Discussion
Document', HMSO.
R. Huws-Jones (1971), 'The Doctor and the Social Ser-
vices', Athlone Press.
Department of Health and Social Security (1976), 'Preven-
tion and Health: Everybody's Business', HMSO.
M. Marshall, M. Preston-Shoot and E. Winnicott (1979),
'Teamwork: For and Against', BASW Publications.

Notes

CHAPTER 2 COLLABORATION BETWEEN DOCTORS AND
SOCIAL WORKERS

1 Sir George Newman (1931), 'Preventive Medicine for
  Medical Students', Oxford University Press.
2 D. Robinson (1971), 'The Process of Becoming Ill',
  Routledge & Kegan Paul.
3 'Report of the Royal Commission on Medical Education'
  (1968), Cmnd 3569, HMSO.
4 C.H. Waddington (1941), 'The Scientific Attitude',
  Penguin.
5 J. Garrad (1966), On the margin of the impossible,
  'Medical Social Work', June.

CHAPTER 3 INTERACTING FACTORS IN HEALTH CARE
- TWO ILLUSTRATIONS

1 D. Robinson (1971), 'The Process of Becoming Ill',
  Routledge & Kegan Paul.

CHAPTER 4 HEALTH IN RELATION TO AGE

1 'The Report of the Committee on Child Health Services'
  (1978), Cmnd 6684, HMSO.
2 'The Report of the Committee on Child Health Services',
  op. cit.
3 DHSS (1980), 'Inequalities in Health', HMSO.
4 P.M. McWheeney and J.L. Emery (1975), Unexpected
  Postneonatal Deaths due to Recognisable Disease,

'Archives of Disease in Childhood', vol. 50, pt 3, pp. 191-96.

5 M. Rutter, J. Tizard and K. Whitmore (1970), 'Education, Health and Behaviour', Longman.

6 A. Kushlick and R. Blunden (1974), The Epidemiology of Mental Subnormality, in 'Mental Deficiency: The Changing Outlook', ed. A.M. Clark and A.D.B. Clarke, 3rd edition, Methuen.

7 M. Rutter (1972), 'Maternal Deprivation Reassessed', Penguin.

8 A. Freud, J. Goldstein and A.J. Solnit (1973), 'Beyond the Best Interests of the Child', Methuen.

9 S. Olshansky (1965), Chronic Sorrow: a response to having a mentally defective child, in 'Social Work with Families', ed. E. Younghusband, Allen & Unwin.

10 R. Lansdown (1980), 'More than Sympathy', Tavistock.

11 S. Hewett (1970), 'The Family and the Handicapped Child', Allen & Unwin.

12 M. Fox (1975), 'They Get This Training But They Don't Really Know How You Feel', National Fund for Research into Crippling Diseases.

13 'The Report of the Committee on Child Health Services', p. 346.

14 R. Davies, N. Butler and H. Goldstein (1972), 'From Birth to Seven', Second Report of the National Child Development Study, Longman.

15 J.W.B. Douglas and J.M. Blomfield (1958), 'Children under Five', Allen & Unwin.

16 M. Schofield (1973), 'The Sexual Behaviour of Young Adults', Allen Lane.

17 J. Dominian (1968), 'Marital Breakdown', Penguin.

18 DHSS (1980), 'Inequalities in Health', HMSO.

19 J.N. Morris, S.P.W. Chade, C. Adam et al. (1973), Vigorous Exercise in Leisure Time and the Incidence of Coronary Heart Disease, 'Lancet', 1333-9.

20 Report of a Special Committee of the Royal College of Psychiatrists (1979), 'Alcohol and Alcoholism', Tavistock.

21 M.L. Johnson (1972), Self-perception of Need amongst the Elderly: an Analysis of Illness Behaviour, 'Sociological Review', vol. 20, no. 4.

22 M. Wicks (1978), 'Old and Cold: Hypothermia and Social Policy', Heinemann.

23 E. Ericson (1963), 'Childhood and Society', W.W. Norton.

24 A. Pincus (1967), Reminiscence in Ageing and its Implications for Social Work Practice, 'Social Work', July.
25 DHSS (1978), 'Social Service Teams: The Practitioner's View', HMSO.

CHAPTER 5 SYMPTOMS

1 I. Illich (1976), 'Limits to Medicine', Boyar.
2 T. Szasz (1959), Language and Pain, in S. Ariesti (ed.), 'American Handbook of Psychiatry', Basic Books.
3 R. Dubos (1970), 'Man, Medicine and Environment', Penguin.
4 J. Merskey and F.G. Spear (1967), 'The Psychological and Psychiatric Aspects of Pain', Tindall & Balliere.
5 M. Zborowski (1958), Cultural Components in Response to Pain, 'Journal of Social Issues', vol. 8.
6 J. and E. Newson (1975), 'Seven Years Old in the Home Environment', Allen & Unwin.
7 J. Merskey and F.G. Spear, op. cit.
8 I. Illich, op. cit.
9 Z. Butrym (1967), 'Social Work in Medical Care', Routledge & Kegan Paul.
10 D.W. Winnicott (1958), The Capacity to be Alone, in 'The Maturational Processes and the Facilitating Environment', Tavistock.
11 D.W. Winnicott (1965), 'Family and Individual Development', Hogarth Press.
12 E. Ericson (1963), 'Childhood and Society', 2nd edition, W.W. Norton.
13 J. Tunstall (1966), 'Old and Alone', Routledge & Kegan Paul.
14 P. Marris (1958), 'Widows and their Families', Routledge & Kegan Paul.
15 P. Sainsbury et al. (1966), 'Suicide and Community Care', Chapman & Hall.
16 G.W. Brown and T. Harris (1978), 'Social Origins of Depression', Tavistock.
17 Z. Butrym (1967), op. cit.

CHAPTER 6 DISEASES OF PARTICULAR IMPORTANCE

1 C. Saunders (ed.) (1978), 'The Management of Terminal Disease', Arnold.

2 E.M. Goldberg (1958), 'Family Influences and Psychosomatic Illness', Tavistock.

CHAPTER 7 THE MANAGEMENT OF CHRONIC SICKNESS AND DISABILITY AND OF TERMINAL ILLNESS

1 'The Report of the Committee on Child Health Services'
(1981), Cmnd 6684, HMSO.
2 British Association of Social Workers (1981), 'Guidelines on Social Work with Disabled People', BASW.
3 E. Goffman (1969), 'Stigma', Penguin.
4 P. Schilder (1935), 'The Image and Appearance of the
Human Body', Routledge & Kegan Paul.
5 Disability Alliance (1979), 'Disability Rights Handbook'.
6 J.A. Muir Gray (1981), Caring for the Religious
Aspects of Disability, 'The Times', 7 February.
7 Department of Health and Social Security (1972), 'Symposium on the Care of the Dying', HMSO, p. 44.
8 G. Gorer (1965), 'Death, Grief and Mourning in Contemporary Britain', Cresset.
9 Council of Europe (1976), 'Statement on the Rights of
the Sick and Dying'.
10 Department of Health and Social Security (1972), op.
cit., p. 53.
11 C. Saunders (ed.) (1978), 'The Management of Terminal
Disease', Arnold.
12 E. Kuebler-Ross (1970), 'On Death and Dying',
Tavistock.
13 J. Hinton (1967), 'Death', Penguin.
14 C. Murray-Parkes (1972), 'Bereavement and Studies in
Grief in Adult Life', Tavistock.
15 S. de Beauvoir (1966), 'A Very Easy Death', Penguin.
16 C. Saunders (1969), The Moment of Truth: The Care of
the Dying, in L. Pearson (ed.), 'Death and Dying Care',
Western Reserve University Press.
17 D.W. Rees (1972), Distress of Dying, 'British Medical
Journal', vol. 3, pp. 105-7.

CHAPTER 8 HEALTH CARE SETTINGS

1 J.C. Morrell (1976), 'An Introduction to Primary Medical Care', Churchill Livingstone.
2 K. Hodgkin (1978), 'Towards Earlier Diagnosis in Primary Care', 4th edition, Churchill Livingstone.

3 J.A.S. Forman and E.M. Fairbairn (1968), 'Social Casework in General Practice', Oxford University Press.
4 E.M. Goldberg and J.E. Neill (1972), 'Social Work in General Practice', Allen & Unwin.
5 Leeqwenhorst Working Party (1974), 'The General Practitioner in Europe', obtainable from the Royal College of Practitioners, London.
6 Department of Health and Social Security (1976), 'Annual Report', HMSO.
7 Department of Health and Social Security (1974), 'Health and Personal Social Services Statistics', HMSO.
8 Royal College of General Practitioners (1979), 'Trends in General Practice'.
9 J. Clark (1973), 'A Family Visitor', Royal College of Nurses.
10 J.A.S. Forman and E.M. Fairbairn (1968), op. cit.
11 E.M. Goldberg and J.E. Neill (1972), op. cit.
12 Royal College of General Practitioners (1979), op. cit.
13 J.R. Butler (1980), How Many Patients? 'Occasional Papers in Social Administration', no. 64, Bedford Square Press.
14 M. Courtenay et al. (1974), Frequent Attendance in a Family Practice, 'Journal of the Royal College of Practitioners', vol. 24, p. 251.
15 J.A. Forbes et al. (1967), Study of the Demand for Urgent Treatment in General Practice, 'British Medical Journal', vol. 3, p. 856.
16 A. MacDonald and I.G. McLean (1971), Study of the Work of General Practitioners, 'Practitioner', vol. 207, p. 680.
17 A. Cartwright (1967), 'Patients and Doctors', Routledge & Kegan Paul; A. Cartwright and R. Anderson (1981), 'General Practice Revisited: a second study of patients and their doctors', Tavistock.
18 A. Cartwright (1967) and (1981), op. cit.
19 'Report of the Committee on Local Authority and Allied Personal Social Services' (1968), Cmnd 3703, HMSO.
20 T. Bamford (1978), Comment, 'Social Work To-day', 7 May.
21 Department of Health and Social Security (1970), 'The Future Structure of the National Health Service', HMSO.
22 W.L. Tongue, D.S. James and S.M. Hillam (1975), 'Families without Hope, A controlled study of 33 Problem

Families', Headley Brothers Ltd, for Royal College of
Psychiatrists.

Index

Routledge Social Science Series

Routledge & Kegan Paul   London, Henley and Boston

39 Store Street,
London WC1E 7DD
Broadway House,
Newtown Road,
Henley-on-Thames,
Oxon RG9 1EN
9 Park Street,
Boston, Mass. 02108

Contents

*Authors wishing to submit manuscripts for any series
in this catalogue should send them to the Social Science Editor,
Routledge & Kegan Paul Ltd, 39 Store Street,
London WC1E 7DD.*
● *Books so marked are available in paperback.*
○ *Books so marked are available in paperback only.*
*All books are in metric Demy 8vo format (216 × 138mm approx.)
unless otherwise stated.*

International Library of Sociology
General Editor   John Rex

GENERAL SOCIOLOGY

Barnsley, J. H. The Social Reality of Ethics. *464 pp.*
Brown, Robert. Explanation in Social Science. *208 pp.*
● Rules and Laws in Sociology. *192 pp.*
Bruford, W. H. Chekhov and His Russia. *A Sociological Study. 244 pp.*
Burton, F. and **Carlen, P.** Official Discourse. *On Discourse Analysis, Government Publications, Ideology. About 140 pp.*
Cain, Maureen E. Society and the Policeman's Role. *326 pp.*
● **Fletcher, Colin.** Beneath the Surface. *An Account of Three Styles of Sociological Research. 221 pp.*
Gibson, Quentin. The Logic of Social Enquiry. *240 pp.*
Glassner, B. Essential Interactionism. *208 pp.*
Glucksmann, M. Structuralist Analysis in Contemporary Social Thought. *212 pp.*
Gurvitch, Georges. Sociology of Law. *Foreword by Roscoe Pound. 264 pp.*
Hinkle, R. Founding Theory of American Sociology 1881–1913. *About 350 pp.*
Homans, George C. Sentiments and Activities. *336 pp.*
Johnson, Harry M. Sociology: *A Systematic Introduction. Foreword by Robert K. Merton. 710 pp.*
● **Keat, Russell** and **Urry, John.** Social Theory as Science. *278 pp.*
Mannheim, Karl. Essays on Sociology and Social Psychology. *Edited by Paul Kecskemeti. With Editorial Note by Adolph Lowe. 344 pp.*
Martindale, Don. The Nature and Types of Sociological Theory. *292 pp.*
● **Maus, Heinz.** A Short History of Sociology. *234 pp.*
Myrdal, Gunnar. Value in Social Theory: *A Collection of Essays on Methodology. Edited by Paul Streeten. 332 pp.*
Ogburn, William F. and **Nimkoff, Meyer F.** A Handbook of Sociology. *Preface by Karl Mannheim. 656 pp. 46 figures. 35 tables.*
Parsons, Talcott and **Smelser, Neil J.** Economy and Society: *A Study in the Integration of Economic and Social Theory. 362 pp.*
Payne, G., Dingwall, R., Payne, J. and **Carter, M.** Sociology and Social Research. *About 250 pp.*
Podgórecki, A. Practical Social Sciences. *About 200 pp.*
Podgórecki, A. and **Łos, M.** Multidimensional Sociology. *268 pp.*
Raffel, S. Matters of Fact. *A Sociological Inquiry. 152 pp.*
● **Rex, John.** Key Problems of Sociological Theory. *220 pp.*
Sociology and the Demystification of the Modern World. *282 pp.*
● **Rex, John.** (Ed.) Approaches to Sociology. *Contributions by Peter Abell, Frank Bechhofer, Basil Bernstein, Ronald Fletcher, David Frisby, Miriam Glucksmann, Peter Lassman, Herminio Martins, John Rex, Roland Robertson, John Westergaard and Jock Young. 302 pp.*
Rigby, A. Alternative Realities. *352 pp.*
Roche, M. Phenomenology, Language and the Social Sciences. *374 pp.*
Sahay, A. Sociological Analysis. *220 pp.*
Strasser, Hermann. The Normative Structure of Sociology. *Conservative and Emancipatory Themes in Social Thought. About 340 pp.*
Strong, P. Ceremonial Order of the Clinic. *267 pp.*
Urry, John. Reference Groups and the Theory of Revolution. *244 pp.*
Weinberg, E. Development of Sociology in the Soviet Union. *173 pp.*

FOREIGN CLASSICS OF SOCIOLOGY

● **Gerth, H. H.** and **Mills, C. Wright.** From Max Weber: *Essays in Sociology. 502 pp.*

● **Tönnies, Ferdinand.** Community and Association *(Gemeinschaft und Gesell-schaft).|Translated and Supplemented by Charles P. Loomis. Foreword by Pitirim A. Sorokin. 334 pp.*

SOCIAL STRUCTURE

Andreski, Stanislav. Military Organization and Society. *Foreword by Professor A. R. Radcliffe-Brown. 226 pp. 1 folder.*

Broom, L., Lancaster Jones, F., McDonnell, P. and **Williams, T.** The Inheritance of Inequality. *About 180 pp.*

Carlton, Eric. Ideology and Social Order. *Foreword by Professor Philip Abrahams. About 320 pp.*

Clegg, S. and **Dunkerley, D.** Organization, Class and Control. *614 pp.*

Coontz, Sydney H. Population Theories and the Economic Interpretation. *202 pp.*

Coser, Lewis. The Functions of Social Conflict. *204 pp.*

Crook, I. and **D.** The First Years of the Yangyi Commune. *304 pp., illustrated.*

Dickie-Clark, H. F. Marginal Situation: *A Sociological Study of a Coloured Group. 240 pp. 11 tables.*

Giner, S. and **Archer, M. S.** (Eds) Contemporary Europe: *Social Structures and Cultural Patterns, 336 pp.*

● **Glaser, Barney** and **Strauss, Anselm L.** Status Passage: *A Formal Theory. 212 pp.*

Glass, D. V. (Ed.) Social Mobility in Britain. *Contributions by J. Berent, T. Bottomore, R. C. Chambers, J. Floud, D. V. Glass, J. R. Hall, H. T. Himmelweit, R. K. Kelsall, F. M. Martin, C. A. Moser, R. Mukherjee and W. Ziegel. 420 pp.*

Kelsall, R. K. Higher Civil Servants in Britain: *From 1870 to the Present Day. 268 pp. 31 tables.*

● **Lawton, Denis.** Social Class, Language and Education. *192 pp.*

McLeish, John. The Theory of Social Change: *Four Views Considered. 128 pp.*

● **Marsh, David C.** The Changing Social Structure of England and Wales, 1871–1961. *Revised edition. 288 pp.*

Menzies, Ken. Talcott Parsons and the Social Image of Man. *About 208 pp.*

● **Mouzelis, Nicos.** Organization and Bureaucracy. *An Analysis of Modern Theories. 240 pp.*

● **Ossowski, Stanislaw.** Class Structure in the Social Consciousness. *210 pp.*

● **Podgórecki, Adam.** Law and Society. *302 pp.*

Renner, Karl. Institutions of Private Law and Their Social Functions. *Edited, with an Introduction and Notes, by O. Kahn-Freud. Translated by Agnes Schwarzschild. 316 pp.*

Rex, J. and **Tomlinson, S.** Colonial Immigrants in a British City. *A Class Analysis. 368 pp.*

Smooha, S. Israel: Pluralism and Conflict. *472 pp.*

Wesolowski, W. Class, Strata and Power. *Trans. and with Introduction by G. Kolankiewicz. 160 pp.*

Zureik, E. Palestinians in Israel. *A Study in Internal Colonialism. 264 pp.*

SOCIOLOGY AND POLITICS

Acton, T. A. Gypsy Politics and Social Change. *316 pp.*

Burton, F. Politics of Legitimacy. *Struggles in a Belfast Community. 250 pp.*

Crook, I. and **D.** Revolution in a Chinese Village. *Ten Mile Inn. 216 pp., illustrated.*

Etzioni-Halevy, E. Political Manipulation and Administrative Power. *A Comparative Study. About 200 pp.*

Fielding, N. The National Front. *About 250 pp.*

● **Hechter, Michael.** Internal Colonialism. *The Celtic Fringe in British National Development, 1536–1966. 380 pp.*

Kornhauser, William. The Politics of Mass Society. *272 pp. 20 tables.*

Korpi, W. The Working Class in Welfare Capitalism. *Work, Unions and Politics in Sweden. 472 pp.*

Kroes, R. Soldiers and Students. *A Study of Right- and Left-wing Students. 174 pp.*

Martin, Roderick. Sociology of Power. *About 272 pp.*

Merquior, J. G. Rousseau and Weber. *A Study in the Theory of Legitimacy. About 288 pp.*

Myrdal, Gunnar. The Political Element in the Development of Economic Theory. *Translated from the German by Paul Streeten. 282 pp.*

Varma, B. N. The Sociology and Politics of Development. *A Theoretical Study. 236 pp.*

Wong, S.-L. Sociology and Socialism in Contemporary China. *160 pp.*

Wootton, Graham. Workers, Unions and the State. *188 pp.*

CRIMINOLOGY

Ancel, Marc. Social Defence: *A Modern Approach to Criminal Problems. Foreword by Leon Radzinowicz. 240 pp.*

Athens, L. Violent Criminal Acts and Actors. *104 pp.*

Cain, Maureen E. Society and the Policeman's Role. *326 pp.*

Cloward, Richard A. and **Ohlin, Lloyd E.** Delinquency and Opportunity: *A Theory of Delinquent Gangs. 248 pp.*

Downes, David M. The Delinquent Solution. *A Study in Subcultural Theory. 296 pp.*

Friedlander, Kate. The Psycho-Analytical Approach to Juvenile Delinquency: *Theory, Case Studies, Treatment. 320 pp.*

Gleuck, Sheldon and **Eleanor.** Family Environment and Delinquency. *With the statistical assistance of Rose W. Kneznek. 340 pp.*

Lopez-Rey, Manuel. Crime. *An Analytical Appraisal. 288 pp.*

Mannheim, Hermann. Comparative Criminology: *A Text Book. Two volumes. 442 pp. and 380 pp.*

Morris, Terence. The Criminal Area: *A Study in Social Ecology. Foreword by Hermann Mannheim. 232 pp. 25 tables. 4 maps.*

Rock, Paul. Making People Pay. *338 pp.*

● **Taylor, Ian, Walton, Paul** and **Young, Jock.** The New Criminology. *For a Social Theory of Deviance. 325 pp.*

● **Taylor, Ian, Walton, Paul** and **Young, Jock.** (Eds) Critical Criminology. *268 pp.*

SOCIAL PSYCHOLOGY

Bagley, Christopher. The Social Psychology of the Epileptic Child. *320 pp.*

Brittan, Arthur. Meanings and Situations. *224 pp.*

Carroll, J. Break-Out from the Crystal Palace. *200 pp.*

● **Fleming, C. M.** Adolescence: Its Social Psychology. *With an Introduction to recent findings from the fields of Anthropology, Physiology, Medicine, Psychometrics and Sociometry. 288 pp.*

● The Social Psychology of Education: *An Introduction and Guide to Its Study. 136 pp.*

Linton, Ralph. The Cultural Background of Personality. *132 pp.*

● **Mayo, Elton.** The Social Problems of an Industrial Civilization. *With an Appendix on the Political Problem. 180 pp.*

Ottaway, A. K. C. Learning Through Group Experience. *176 pp.*

Plummer, Ken. Sexual Stigma. *An Interactionist Account. 254 pp.*

● **Rose, Arnold M.** (Ed.) Human Behaviour and Social Processes: *an Interactionist Approach. Contributions by Arnold M. Rose, Ralph H. Turner, Anselm Strauss, Everett C. Hughes, E. Franklin Frazier, Howard S. Becker et al. 696 pp.*

Smelser, Neil J. Theory of Collective Behaviour. *448 pp.*

Stephenson, Geoffrey M. The Development of Conscience. *128 pp.*

Young, Kimball. Handbook of Social Psychology. *658 pp. 16 figures. 10 tables.*

SOCIOLOGY OF THE FAMILY

Bell, Colin R. Middle Class Families: *Social and Geographical Mobility. 224 pp.*
Burton, Lindy. Vulnerable Children. *272 pp.*
Gavron, Hannah. The Captive Wife: *Conflicts of Household Mothers. 190 pp.*
George, Victor and **Wilding, Paul.** Motherless Families. *248 pp.*
Klein, Josephine. Samples from English Cultures.
   1. Three Preliminary Studies and Aspects of Adult Life in England. *447 pp.*
   2. Child-Rearing Practices and Index. *247 pp.*
Klein, Viola. The Feminine Character. *History of an Ideology. 244 pp.*
McWhinnie, Alexina M. Adopted Children. *How They Grow Up. 304 pp.*
● **Morgan, D. H. J.** Social Theory and the Family. *About 320 pp.*
● **Myrdal, Alva** and **Klein, Viola.** Women's Two Roles: *Home and Work. 238 pp.*
   27 tables.
Parsons, Talcott and **Bales, Robert F.** Family: Socialization and Interaction Process. *In collaboration with James Olds, Morris Zelditch and Philip E. Slater. 456 pp. 50 figures and tables.*

SOCIAL SERVICES

Bastide, Roger. The Sociology of Mental Disorder. *Translated from the French by Jean McNeil. 260 pp.*
Carlebach, Julius. Caring For Children in Trouble. *266 pp.*
George, Victor. Foster Care. *Theory and Practice. 234 pp.*
   Social Security: *Beveridge and After. 258 pp.*
George, V. and **Wilding, P.** Motherless Families. *248 pp.*
● **Goetschius, George W.** Working with Community Groups. *256 pp.*
Goetschius, George W. and **Tash, Joan.** Working with Unattached Youth. *416 pp.*
Heywood, Jean S. Children in Care. *The Development of the Service for the Deprived Child. Third revised edition. 284 pp.*
King, Roy D., Ranes, Norma V. and **Tizard, Jack.** Patterns of Residential Care. *356 pp.*
Leigh, John. Young People and Leisure. *256 pp.*
● **Mays, John.** (Ed.) Penelope Hall's Social Services of England and Wales. *368 pp.*
Morris, Mary. Voluntary Work and the Welfare State. *300 pp.*
Nokes, P. L. The Professional Task in Welfare Practice. *152 pp.*
Timms, Noel. Psychiatric Social Work in Great Britain (1939–1962). *280 pp.*
●   Social Casework: *Principles and Practice. 256 pp.*

SOCIOLOGY OF EDUCATION

Banks, Olive. Parity and Prestige in English Secondary Education: a Study in Educational Sociology. *272 pp.*
● **Blyth, W. A. L.** English Primary Education. *A Sociological Description.*
   2. Background. *168 pp.*
Collier, K. G. The Social Purposes of Education: *Personal and Social Values in Education. 268 pp.*
Evans, K. M. Sociometry and Education. *158 pp.*
● **Ford, Julienne.** Social Class and the Comprehensive School. *192 pp.*
Foster, P. J. Education and Social Change in Ghana. *336 pp. 3 maps.*
Fraser, W. R. Education and Society in Modern France. *150 pp.*
Grace, Gerald R. Role Conflict and the Teacher. *150 pp.*
Hans, Nicholas. New Trends in Education in the Eighteenth Century. *278 pp. 19 tables.*
●   Comparative Education: *A Study of Educational Factors and Traditions. 360 pp.*
● **Hargreaves, David.** Interpersonal Relations and Education. *432 pp.*
●   Social Relations in a Secondary School. *240 pp.*
   School Organization and Pupil Involvement. *A Study of Secondary Schools.*

- **Mannheim, Karl** and **Stewart, W. A. C.** An Introduction to the Sociology of Education. *206 pp.*
- **Musgrove, F.** Youth and the Social Order. *176 pp.*
- **Ottaway, A. K. C.** Education and Society: An Introduction to the Sociology of Education. *With an Introduction by W. O. Lester Smith. 212 pp.*

Peers, Robert. Adult Education: *A Comparative Study. Revised edition. 398 pp.*

Stratta, Erica. The Education of Borstal Boys. *A Study of their Educational Experiences prior to, and during, Borstal Training. 256 pp.*

- **Taylor, P. H., Reid, W. A.** and **Holley, B. J.** The English Sixth Form. *A Case Study in Curriculum Research. 198 pp.*

SOCIOLOGY OF CULTURE

Eppel, E. M. and **M.** Adolescents and Morality: *A Study of some Moral Values and Dilemmas of Working Adolescents in the Context of a changing Climate of Opinion. Foreword by W. J. H. Sprott. 268 pp. 39 tables.*

- **Fromm, Erich.** The Fear of Freedom. *286 pp.*
- The Sane Society. *400 pp.*

Johnson, L. The Cultural Critics. *From Matthew Arnold to Raymond Williams. 233 pp.*

Mannheim, Karl. Essays on the Sociology of Culture. *Edited by Ernst Mannheim in co-operation with Paul Kecskemeti. Editorial Note by Adolph Lowe. 280 pp.*

Merquior, J. G. The Veil and the Mask. *Essays on Culture and Ideology. Foreword by Ernest Gellner. 140 pp.*

Zijderfeld, A. C. On Clichés. *The Supersedure of Meaning by Function in Modernity. 150 pp.*

SOCIOLOGY OF RELIGION

Argyle, Michael and **Beit-Hallahmi, Benjamin.** The Social Psychology of Religion. *256 pp.*

Glasner, Peter E. The Sociology of Secularisation. *A Critique of a Concept. 146 pp.*

Hall, J. R. The Ways Out. *Utopian Communal Groups in an Age of Babylon. 280 pp.*

Ranson, S., Hinings, B. and **Bryman, A.** Clergy, Ministers and Priests. *216 pp.*

Stark, Werner. The Sociology of Religion. *A Study of Christendom.*
    Volume II. *Sectarian Religion. 368 pp.*
    Volume III. *The Universal Church. 464 pp.*
    Volume IV. *Types of Religious Man. 352 pp.*
    Volume V. *Types of Religious Culture. 464 pp.*

Turner, B. S. Weber and Islam. *216 pp.*

Watt, W. Montgomery. Islam and the Integration of Society. *320 pp.*

SOCIOLOGY OF ART AND LITERATURE

Jarvie, Ian C. Towards a Sociology of the Cinema. *A Comparative Essay on the Structure and Functioning of a Major Entertainment Industry. 405 pp.*

Rust, Frances S. Dance in Society. *An Analysis of the Relationships between the Social Dance and Society in England from the Middle Ages to the Present Day. 256 pp. 8 pp. of plates.*

Schücking, L. L. The Sociology of Literary Taste. *112 pp.*

Wolff, Janet. Hermeneutic Philosophy and the Sociology of Art. *150 pp.*

SOCIOLOGY OF KNOWLEDGE

Diesing, P. Patterns of Discovery in the Social Sciences. *262 pp.*

● **Douglas, J. D.** (Ed.) Understanding Everyday Life. *370 pp.*
● **Hamilton, P.** Knowledge and Social Structure. *174 pp.*
Jarvie, I. C. Concepts and Society. *232 pp.*
Mannheim, Karl. Essays on the Sociology of Knowledge. *Edited by Paul Kecskemeti. Editorial Note by Adolph Lowe. 353 pp.*
Remmling, Gunter W. The Sociology of Karl Mannheim. *With a Bibliographical Guide to the Sociology of Knowledge, Ideological Analysis, and Social Planning. 255 pp.*
Remmling, Gunter W. (Ed.) Towards the Sociology of Knowledge. *Origin and Development of a Sociological Thought Style. 463 pp.*
Scheler, M. Problems of a Sociology of Knowledge. *Trans. by M. S. Frings. Edited and with an Introduction by K. Stikkers. 232 pp.*

URBAN SOCIOLOGY

Aldridge, M. The British New Towns. *A Programme Without a Policy. 232 pp.*
Ashworth, William. The Genesis of Modern British Town Planning: *A Study in Economic and Social History of the Nineteenth and Twentieth Centuries. 288 pp.*
Brittan, A. The Privatised World. *196 pp.*
Cullingworth, J. B. Housing Needs and Planning Policy: *A Restatement of the Problems of Housing Need and 'Overspill' in England and Wales. 232 pp. 44 tables. 8 maps.*
Dickinson, Robert E. City and Region: *A Geographical Interpretation. 608 pp. 125 figures.*
The West European City: *A Geographical Interpretation. 600 pp. 129 maps. 29 plates.*
Humphreys, Alexander J. New Dubliners: *Urbanization and the Irish Family. Foreword by George C. Homans. 304 pp.*
Jackson, Brian. Working Class Community: *Some General Notions raised by a Series of Studies in Northern England. 192 pp.*
● **Mann, P. H.** An Approach to Urban Sociology. *240 pp.*
Mellor, J. R. Urban Sociology in an Urbanized Society. *326 pp.*
Morris, R. N. and **Mogey, J.** The Sociology of Housing. *Studies at Berinsfield. 232 pp. 4 pp. plates.*
Mullan, R. Stevenage Ltd. *About 250 pp.*
Rex, J. and **Tomlinson, S.** Colonial Immigrants in a British City. *A Class Analysis. 368 pp.*
Rosser, C. and **Harris, C.** The Family and Social Change. *A Study of Family and Kinship in a South Wales Town. 352 pp. 8 maps.*
● **Stacey, Margaret, Batsone, Eric, Bell, Colin** and **Thurcott, Anne.** Power, Persistence and Change. *A Second Study of Banbury. 196 pp.*

RURAL SOCIOLOGY

Mayer, Adrian C. Peasants in the Pacific. *A Study of Fiji Indian Rural Society. 248 pp. 20 plates.*
Williams, W. M. The Sociology of an English Village: *Gosforth. 272 pp. 12 figures. 13 tables.*

SOCIOLOGY OF INDUSTRY AND DISTRIBUTION

Dunkerley, David. The Foreman. *Aspects of Task and Structure. 192 pp.*
Eldridge, J. E. T. Industrial Disputes. *Essays in the Sociology of Industrial Relations. 288 pp.*
Hollowell, Peter G. The Lorry Driver. *272 pp.*
● **Oxaal, I., Barnett, T.** and **Booth, D.** (Eds) Beyond the Sociology of Development.

Economy and Society in Latin America and Africa. 295 pp.
Smelser, Neil J. Social Change in the Industrial Revolution: *An Application of Theory to the Lancashire Cotton Industry, 1770–1840. 468 pp. 12 figures. 14 tables.*
Watson, T. J. The Personnel Managers. *A Study in the Sociology of Work and Employment, 262 pp.*

ANTHROPOLOGY

Brandel-Syrier, Mia. Reeftown Elite. *A Study of Social Mobility in a Modern African Community on the Reef. 376 pp.*
Dickie-Clark, H. F. The Marginal Situation. *A Sociological Study of a Coloured Group. 236 pp.*
Dube, S. C. Indian Village. *Foreword by Morris Edward Opler. 276 pp. 4 plates.*
India's Changing Villages: *Human Factors in Community Development. 260 pp. 8 plates. 1 map.*
Fei, H.-T. Peasant Life in China. *A Field Study of Country Life in the Yangtze Valley. With a foreword by Bronislaw Malinowski. 328 pp. 16 pp. plates.*
Firth, Raymond. Malay Fishermen. *Their Peasant Economy. 420 pp. 17 pp. plates.*
Gulliver, P. H. Social Control in an African Society: a Study of the Arusha, Agricultural Masai of Northern Tanganyika. *320 pp. 8 plates. 10 figures.* Family Herds. *288 pp.*
Jarvie, Ian C. The Revolution in Anthropology. *268 pp.*
Little, Kenneth L. Mende of Sierra Leone. *308 pp. and folder.*
Negroes in Britain. *With a New Introduction and Contemporary Study by Leonard Bloom. 320 pp.*
Tambs-Lyche, H. London Patidars. *About 180 pp.*
Madan, G. R. Western Sociologists on Indian Society. *Marx, Spencer, Weber, Durkheim, Pareto. 384 pp.*
Mayer, A. C. Peasants in the Pacific. *A Study of Fiji Indian Rural Society. 248 pp.*
Meer, Fatima. Race and Suicide in South Africa. *325 pp.*
Smith, Raymond T. The Negro Family in British Guiana: *Family Structure and Social Status in the Villages. With a Foreword by Meyer Fortes. 314 pp. 8 plates. 1 figure. 4 maps.*

SOCIOLOGY AND PHILOSOPHY

Adriaansens, H. Talcott Parsons and the Conceptual Dilemma. *About 224 pp.*
Barnsley, John H. The Social Reality of Ethics. *A Comparative Analysis of Moral Codes. 448 pp.*
Diesing, Paul. Patterns of Discovery in the Social Sciences. *362 pp.*
● **Douglas, Jack D.** (Ed.) Understanding Everyday Life. *Toward the Reconstruction of Sociological Knowledge. Contributions by Alan F. Blum, Aaron W. Cicourel, Norman K. Denzin, Jack D. Douglas, John Heeren, Peter McHugh, Peter K. Manning, Melvin Power, Matthew Speier, Roy Turner, D. Lawrence Wieder, Thomas P. Wilson and Don H. Zimmerman. 370 pp.*
Gorman, Robert A. The Dual Vision. *Alfred Schutz and the Myth of Phenomenological Social Science. 240 pp.*
Jarvie, Ian C. Concepts and Society. *216 pp.*
Kilminster, R. Praxis and Method. *A Sociological Dialogue with Lukács, Gramsci and the Early Frankfurt School. 334 pp.*
● **Pelz, Werner.** The Scope of Understanding in Sociology. *Towards a More Radical Reorientation in the Social Humanistic Sciences. 283 pp.*
Roche, Maurice. Phenomenology, Language and the Social Sciences. *371 pp.*
Sahay, Arun. Sociological Analysis. *212 pp.*
● **Slater, P.** Origin and Significance of the Frankfurt School. *A Marxist Perspective. 185 pp.*

Spurling, L. Phenomenology and the Social World. *The Philosophy of Merleau-Ponty and its Relation to the Social Sciences. 222 pp.*
Wilson, H. T. The American Ideology. *Science, Technology and Organization as Modes of Rationality. 368 pp.*

International Library of Anthropology
General Editor Adam Kuper

● **Ahmed, A. S.** Millennium and Charisma Among Pathans. *A Critical Essay in Social Anthropology. 192 pp.*
Pukhtun Economy and Society. *Traditional Structure and Economic Development. About 360 pp.*
Barth, F. Selected Essays. *Volume I. About 250 pp.* Selected Essays. *Volume II. About 250 pp.*
Brown, Paula. The Chimbu. *A Study of Change in the New Guinea Highlands. 151 pp.*
Foner, N. Jamaica Farewell. *200 pp.*
Gudeman, Stephen. Relationships, Residence and the Individual. *A Rural Panamanian Community. 288 pp. 11 plates, 5 figures, 2 maps, 10 tables.*
The Demise of a Rural Economy. *From Subsistence to Capitalism in a Latin American Village. 160 pp.*
Hamnett, Ian. Chieftainship and Legitimacy. *An Anthropological Study of Executive Law in Lesotho. 163 pp.*
Hanson, F. Allan. Meaning in Culture. *127 pp.*
Hazan, H. The Limbo People. *A Study of the Constitution of the Time Universe Among the Aged. About 192 pp.*
Humphreys, S. C. Anthropology and the Greeks. *288 pp.*
Karp, I. Fields of Change Among the Iteso of Kenya. *140 pp.*
Lloyd, P. C. Power and Independence. *Urban Africans' Perception of Social Inequality. 264 pp.*
Parry, J. P. Caste and Kinship in Kangra. *352 pp. Illustrated.*
Pettigrew, Joyce. Robber Noblemen. *A Study of the Political System of the Sikh Jats. 284 pp.*
Street, Brian V. The Savage in Literature. *Representations of 'Primitive' Society in English Fiction, 1858–1920. 207 pp.*
Van Den Berghe, Pierre L. Power and Privilege at an African University. *278 pp.*

International Library of Phenomenology and Moral Sciences
General Editor John O'Neill

Apel, K.-O. Towards a Transformation of Philosophy. *308 pp.*
Bologh, R. W. Dialectical Phenomenology. *Marx's Method. 287 pp.*
Fekete, J. The Critical Twilight. *Explorations in the Ideology of Anglo-American Literary Theory from Eliot to McLuhan. 300 pp.*
Medina, A. Reflection, Time and the Novel. *Towards a Communicative Theory of Literature. 143 pp.*

International Library of Social Policy
General Editor Kathleen Jones

Bayley, M. Mental Handicap and Community Care. *426 pp.*
Bottoms, A. E. and **McClean, J. D.** Defendants in the Criminal Process. *284 pp.*
Bradshaw, J. The Family Fund. *An Initiative in Social Policy. About 224 pp.*

Butler, J. R. Family Doctors and Public Policy. *208 pp.*
Davies, Martin. Prisoners of Society. *Attitudes and Aftercare. 204 pp.*
Gittus, Elizabeth. Flats, Families and the Under-Fives. *285 pp.*
Holman, Robert. Trading in Children. *A Study of Private Fostering. 355 pp.*
Jeffs, A. Young People and the Youth Service. *160 pp.*
Jones, Howard and Cornes, Paul. Open Prisons. *288 pp.*
Jones, Kathleen. History of the Mental Health Service. *428 pp.*
Jones, Kathleen with **Brown, John, Cunningham, W. J., Roberts, Julian** and
    Williams, Peter. Opening the Door. *A Study of New Policies for the Mentally
    Handicapped. 278 pp.*
Karn, Valerie. Retiring to the Seaside. *400 pp. 2 maps. Numerous tables.*
King, R. D. and **Elliot, K. W.** Albany: Birth of a Prison—End of an Era. *394 pp.*
Thomas, J. E. The English Prison Officer since 1850: *A Study in Conflict. 258 pp.*
Walton, R. G. Women in Social Work. *303 pp.*
● **Woodward, J.** To Do the Sick No Harm. *A Study of the British Voluntary Hospital
    System to 1875. 234 pp.*

International Library of Welfare and Philosophy
General Editors   Noel Timms and David Watson

● **McDermott, F. E.** (Ed.) Self-Determination in Social Work. *A Collection of Essays
    on Self-determination and Related Concepts by Philosophers and Social Work
    Theorists. Contributors: F. P. Biestek, S. Bernstein, A. Keith-Lucas, D. Sayer,
    H. H. Perelman, C. Whittington, R. F. Stalley, F. E. McDermott, I. Berlin, H. J.
    McCloskey, H. L. A. Hart, J. Wilson, A. I. Melden, S. I. Benn. 254 pp.*
● **Plant, Raymond.** Community and Ideology. *104 pp.*
Ragg, Nicholas M. People Not Cases. *A Philosophical Approach to Social Work.
    168 pp.*
● **Timms, Noel** and **Watson, David.** (Eds) Talking About Welfare. *Readings in
    Philosophy and Social Policy. Contributors: T. H. Marshall, R. B. Brandt, G. H.
    von Wright, K. Nielsen, M. Cranston, R. M. Titmuss, R. S. Downie, E. Telfer, D.
    Donnison, J. Benson, P. Leonard, A. Keith-Lucas, D. Walsh, I. T. Ramsey.
    320 pp.*
● Philosophy in Social Work. *250 pp.*
● **Weale, A.** Equality and Social Policy. *164 pp.*

Library of Social Work
General Editor   Noel Timms

● **Baldock, Peter.** Community Work and Social Work. *140 pp.*
○ **Beedell, Christopher.** Residential Life with Children. *210 pp. Crown 8vo.*
● **Berry, Juliet.** Daily Experience in Residential Life. *A Study of Children and their
    Care-givers. 202 pp.*
○ Social Work with Children. *190 pp. Crown 8vo.*
● **Brearley, C. Paul.** Residential Work with the Elderly. *116 pp.*
● Social Work, Ageing and Society. *126 pp.*
● **Cheetham, Juliet.** Social Work with Immigrants. *240 pp. Crown 8vo.*
● **Cross, Crispin P.** (Ed.) Interviewing and Communication in Social Work.
        *Contributions by C. P. Cross, D. Laurenson, B. Strutt, S. Raven. 192 pp. Crown
        8vo.*

● **Curnock, Kathleen** and **Hardiker, Pauline.** Towards Practice Theory. *Skills and Methods in Social Assessments. 208 pp.*

● **Davies, Bernard.** The Use of Groups in Social Work Practice. *158 pp.*

● **Davies, Martin.** Support Systems in Social Work. *144 pp.*

Ellis, June. (Ed.) West African Families in Britain. *A Meeting of Two Cultures. Contributions by Pat Stapleton, Vivien Biggs. 150 pp. 1 Map.*

● **Hart, John.** Social Work and Sexual Conduct. *230 pp.*

● **Hutten, Joan M.** Short-Term Contracts in Social Work. *Contributions by Stella M. Hall, Elsie Osborne, Mannie Sher, Eva Sternberg, Elizabeth Tuters. 134 pp.*

Jackson, Michael P. and **Valencia, B. Michael.** Financial Aid Through Social Work. *140 pp.*

● **Jones, Howard.** The Residential Community. *A Setting for Social Work. 150 pp.*

● (Ed.) Towards a New Social Work. *Contributions by Howard Jones, D. A. Fowler, J. R. Cypher, R. G. Walton, Geoffrey Mungham, Philip Priestley, Ian Shaw, M. Bartley, R. Deacon, Irwin Epstein, Geoffrey Pearson. 184 pp.*

Jones, Ray and **Pritchard, Colin.** (Eds) Social Work With Adolescents. *Contributions by Ray Jones, Colin Pritchard, Jack Dunham, Florence Rossetti, Andrew Kerslake, John Burns, William Gregory, Graham Templeman, Kenneth E. Reid, Audrey Taylor. About 170 pp.*

○ **Jordon, William.** The Social Worker in Family Situations. *160 pp. Crown 8vo.*

● **Laycock, A. L.** Adolescents and Social Work. *128 pp. Crown 8vo.*

● **Lees, Ray.** Politics and Social Work. *128 pp. Crown 8vo.*

● Research Strategies for Social Welfare. *112 pp. Tables.*

○ **McCullough, M. K.** and **Ely, Peter J.** Social Work with Groups. *127 pp. Crown 8vo.*

● **Moffett, Jonathan.** Concepts in Casework Treatment. *128 pp. Crown 8vo.*

Parsloe, Phyllida. Juvenile Justice in Britain and the United States. *The Balance of Needs and Rights. 336 pp.*

● **Plant, Raymond.** Social and Moral Theory in Casework. *112 pp. Crown 8vo.*

Priestley, Philip, Fears, Denise and **Fuller, Roger.** Justice for Juveniles. *The 1969 Children and Young Persons Act: A Case for Reform? 128 pp.*

● **Pritchard, Colin** and **Taylor, Richard.** Social Work: Reform or Revolution? *170 pp.*

○ **Pugh, Elisabeth.** Social Work in Child Care. *128 pp. Crown 8vo.*

● **Robinson, Margaret.** Schools and Social Work. *282 pp.*

○ **Ruddock, Ralph.** Roles and Relationships. *128 pp. Crown 8vo.*

● **Sainsbury, Eric.** Social Diagnosis in Casework. *118 pp. Crown 8vo.*

● Social Work with Families. *Perceptions of Social Casework among Clients of a Family Service. 188 pp.*

Seed, Philip. The Expansion of Social Work in Britain. *128 pp. Crown 8vo.*

● **Shaw, John.** The Self in Social Work. *124 pp.*

Smale, Gerald G. Prophecy, Behaviour and Change. *An Examination of Self-fulfilling Prophecies in Helping Relationships. 116 pp. Crown 8vo.*

Smith, Gilbert. Social Need. *Policy, Practice and Research. 155 pp.*

● Social Work and the Sociology of Organisations. *124 pp. Revised edition.*

● **Sutton, Carole.** Psychology for Social Workers and Counsellors. *An Introduction. 248 pp.*

● **Timms, Noel.** Language of Social Casework. *122 pp. Crown 8vo.*

● Recording in Social Work. *124 pp. Crown 8vo.*

● **Todd, F. Joan.** Social Work with the Mentally Subnormal. *96 pp. Crown 8vo.*

● **Walrond-Skinner, Sue.** Family Therapy. *The Treatment of Natural Systems. 172 pp.*

● **Warham, Joyce.** An Introduction to Administration for Social Workers. *Revised edition. 112 pp.*

● An Open Case. *The Organisational Context of Social Work. 172 pp.*

○ **Wittenberg, Isca Salzberger.** Psycho-Analytic Insight and Relationships. *A Kleinian Approach. 196 pp. Crown 8vo.*

Primary Socialization, Language and Education
General Editor Basil Bernstein

Adlam, Diana S., *with the assistance of Geoffrey Turner and Lesley Lineker.* Code in Context. *272 pp.*

Bernstein, Basil. Class, Codes and Control. *3 volumes.*
- 1. *Theoretical Studies Towards a Sociology of Language. 254 pp.*
- 2. *Applied Studies Towards a Sociology of Language. 377 pp.*
- 3. *Towards a Theory of Educational Transmission. 167 pp.*

Brandis, W. and **Bernstein, B.** Selection and Control. *176 pp.*

Brandis, Walter and **Henderson, Dorothy.** Social Class, Language and Communication. *288 pp.*

Cook-Gumperz, Jenny. Social Control and Socialization. *A Study of Class Differences in the Language of Maternal Control. 290 pp.*

● **Gahagan, D. M.** and **G. A.** Talk Reform. *Exploration in Language for Infant School Children. 160 pp.*

Hawkins, P. R. Social Class, the Nominal Group and Verbal Strategies. *About 220 pp.*

Robinson, W. P. and **Rackstraw, Susan D. A.** A Question of Answers. *2 volumes. 192 pp. and 180 pp.*

Turner, Geoffrey J. and **Mohan, Bernard A.** A Linguistic Description and Computer Programme for Children's Speech. *208 pp.*

Reports of the Institute of Community Studies

Baker, J. The Neighbourhood Advice Centre. *A Community Project in Camden. 320 pp.*

● **Cartwright, Ann.** Patients and their Doctors. *A Study of General Practice. 304 pp.*

Dench, Geoff. Maltese in London. *A Case-study in the Erosion of Ethnic Consciousness. 302 pp.*

Jackson, Brian and **Marsden, Dennis.** Education and the Working Class: *Some General Themes Raised by a Study of 88 Working-class Children in a Northern Industrial City. 268 pp. 2 folders.*

Marris, Peter. The Experience of Higher Education. *232 pp. 27 tables.*
● Loss and Change. *192 pp.*

Marris, Peter and **Rein, Martin.** Dilemmas of Social Reform. *Poverty and Community Action in the United States. 256 pp.*

Marris, Peter and **Somerset, Anthony.** African Businessmen. *A Study of Entrepreneurship and Development in Kenya. 256 pp.*

Mills, Richard. Young Outsiders: *a Study in Alternative Communities. 216 pp.*

Runciman, W. G. Relative Deprivation and Social Justice. *A Study of Attitudes to Social Inequality in Twentieth-Century England. 352 pp.*

Willmott, Peter. Adolescent Boys in East London. *230 pp.*

Willmott, Peter and **Young, Michael.** Family and Class in a London Suburb. *202 pp. 47 tables.*

Young, Michael and **McGeeney, Patrick.** Learning Begins at Home. *A Study of a Junior School and its Parents. 128 pp.*

Young, Michael and **Willmott, Peter.** Family and Kinship in East London. *Foreword by Richard M. Titmuss. 252 pp. 39 tables.*
The Symmetrical Family. *410 pp.*

Reports of the Institute for Social Studies in Medical Care

Cartwright, Ann, Hockey, Lisbeth and **Anderson, John J.** Life Before Death. *310 pp.*
Dunnell, Karen and **Cartwright, Ann.** Medicine Takers, Prescribers and Hoarders. *190 pp.*
Farrell, C. My Mother Said. . . *A Study of the Way Young People Learned About Sex and Birth Control. 288 pp.*

Medicine, Illness and Society
General Editor W. M. Williams

Hall, David J. Social Relations & Innovation. *Changing the State of Play in Hospitals. 232 pp.*
Hall, David J. and **Stacey, M.** (Eds) Beyond Separation. *234 pp.*
Robinson, David. The Process of Becoming Ill. *142 pp.*
Stacey, Margaret *et al.* Hospitals, Children and Their Families. *The Report of a Pilot Study. 202 pp.*
Stimson, G. V. and **Webb, B.** Going to See the Doctor. *The Consultation Process in General Practice. 155 pp.*

Monographs in Social Theory
General Editor Arthur Brittan

● **Barnes, B.** Scientific Knowledge and Sociological Theory. *192 pp.*
Bauman, Zygmunt. Culture as Praxis. *204 pp.*
● **Dixon, Keith.** Sociological Theory. *Pretence and Possibility. 142 pp.*
The Sociology of Belief. *Fallacy and Foundation. About 160 pp.*
Goff, T. W. Marx and Mead. *Contributions to a Sociology of Knowledge. 176 pp.*
Meltzer, B. N., Petras, J. W. and **Reynolds, L. T.** Symbolic Interactionism. *Genesis, Varieties and Criticisms. 144 pp.*
● **Smith, Anthony D.** The Concept of Social Change. *A Critique of the Functionalist Theory of Social Change. 208 pp.*

Routledge Social Science Journals

The British Journal of Sociology. *Editor – Angus Stewart; Associate Editor – Leslie Sklair. Vol. 1, No. 1 – March 1950 and Quarterly. Roy. 8vo. All back issues available. An international journal publishing original papers in the field of sociology and related areas.*
Community Work. *Edited by David Jones and Marjorie Mayo. 1973. Published annually.*
Economy and Society. *Vol. 1, No. 1. February 1972 and Quarterly. Metric Roy. 8vo. A journal for all social scientists covering sociology, philosophy, anthropology, economics and history. All back numbers available.*

Ethnic and Racial Studies. *Editor – John Stone. Vol. 1 – 1978. Published quarterly.*
Religion. Journal of Religion and Religions. *Chairman of Editorial Board, Ninian Smart. Vol. 1, No. 1, Spring 1971. A journal with an inter-disciplinary approach to the study of the phenomena of religion. All back numbers available.*
Sociology of Health and Illness. *A Journal of Medical Sociology. Editor – Alan Davies; Associate Editor – Ray Jobling. Vol. 1, Spring 1979. Published 3 times per annum.*
Year Book of Social Policy in Britain. *Edited by Kathleen Jones. 1971. Published annually.*

Social and Psychological Aspects of Medical Practice
Editor Trevor Silverstone

Lader, Malcolm. Psychophysiology of Mental Illness. *280 pp.*
● **Silverstone, Trevor** and **Turner, Paul.** Drug Treatment in Psychiatry. *Revised edition. 256 pp.*
Whiteley, J. S. and **Gordon, J.** Group Approaches in Psychiatry. *240 pp.*